The Middle Ages and Early Renaissance

Paintings and Sculptures from the Carlo De Carlo Collection
and other Provenance

This catalogue and the exhibition
were made in collaboration with

ANDREW BUTTERFIELD FINE ART and LISA DE CARLO

MORETTI

The Middle Ages and Early Renaissance
Paintings and Sculptures from the Carlo De Carlo Collection
and other Provenance

Texts by
Daniele Benati
Elisa Camporeale
Andrea De Marchi
Gianluca Del Monaco
Gaudenz Freuler
Aldo Galli
Nicholas Herman
Alberto Lenza
Fabio Massaccesi
Daniela Parenti
Linda Pisani
Nicoletta Pons
Angelo Tartuferi

Centro Di

MORETTI SRL
Piazza degli Ottaviani, 17/r
50123 Firenze
tel. +39 055 2654277
info@morettigallery.com

MORETTI FINE ART LTD
2a-6 Ryder Street, St. James's
London SW1Y 6QA
tel. +44 20 7491 0533
london@morettigallery.com

MORETTI FINE ART LTD
24 East 80th Street
New York, NY 10075
tel. +1 212 249 4987
newyork@morettigallery.com

In collaboration with
ANDREW BUTTERFIELD FINE ART, LCC
197 Broadway
Pleasantville, NY 10570-2342
tel. +1 914 773 4226
info@andrewbutterfield.com

LISA DE CARLO
Via Maggio, 34/r
50125 Firenze
tel. +39 055 293368
lisa.decarlo@virgilio.it

Acknowledgments
Daniele Benati, Miklós Boskovits, Moreno Bucci,
Francesco Caglioti, Keith Christiansen, Everett Fahy,
Carlo Falciani, Arturo Galansino, Giancarlo Gentilini,
Flavio Gianassi, Dillian Gordon, Laurence Kanter,
Antonio Natali, Anna Orlando, Francesco Ortenzi,
Tova Ossad, Xavier Salomon, Giovanni Sarti,
Riccardo Spinelli, Carl Strehlke, Luke Syson,
Stefan Weppelmann.
A special thanks to Alana collection
and all those collectors who kindly allowed
the publication of their works.

CATALOGUE

Edited by
Gabriele Caioni

Concept and selection of works
Fabrizio Moretti

Authors of the entries
Daniele Benati
Elisa Camporeale
Andrea De Marchi
Gianluca Del Monaco
Gaudenz Freuler
Aldo Galli
Nicholas Herman
Alberto Lenza
Fabio Massaccesi
Daniela Parenti
Linda Pisani
Nicoletta Pons
Angelo Tartuferi

English translation by
Anthony Brierley
Frank Dabell (entry no. 16)

Editing: Patrizia Fabbri (Centro Di)

Design and layout: Manola Miniati (Centro Di)

Photographs
Remo Bardazzi
Fototeca Federico Zeri
Paolo and Claudio Giusti
Prudence Cuming Associates Ltd

Photo credits
© Fitzwilliam Museum, Cambridge, fig. 3 p. 46

This catalogue has been published for the exhibition
*The Middle Ages and Early Renaissance. Paintings and
Sculptures from the Carlo De Carlo Collection and other
Provenance* (New York, 18.1.-10.2.2012)

Copyright © 2011
Moretti Srl – Moretti Fine Art Ltd
Published by Centro Di
della Edifimi srl, Firenze
edizioni@centrodi.it
www.centrodi.it

ISBN 978-88-7038-501-4
Printed by Conti Tipocolor S.p.A.
Calenzano, Florence
December 2011

Dedicated to Luciano Bellosi

Every time we manage to put together a substantial nucleus of medieval and Renaissance painting and sculpture it really is a source of enormous satisfaction, for this type of merchandise is difficult to come by these days. In recent years gold-ground and early age paintings have come back into fashion, this being due, I believe, to a rediscovery of their remarkable modernity, or rather, the fact of their being contemporary. Some collectors of modern art have started expanding their collections with gold-ground paintings. But then when you think about it, what is more modern and contemporary than a gold ground? These works, precisely because of their majesty and simplicity, can compete with anything.

Let us not forget that quality art is timeless, and that a Maso di Banco can quite easily be placed beside a Rothko. If for a moment I had to express myself as an art dealer, I would say that we should bear in mind that if you compare the costs of early art with those of modern art, the former is considerably undervalued, and therefore in the world of today it certainly represents an excellent investment.

In this medieval and early Renaissance exhibition I have the good fortune to be able to exhibit a nucleus of really important works coming from Lisa De Carlo, the daughter of Carlo De Carlo, one of the greatest Italian dealers specializing in the early age whose influence on the Italian market has been fundamental. Therefore my heartfelt thanks go to Lisa De Carlo for having given me the opportunity to manage these works and I sincerely hope to honour the charge which has been entrusted to me by her. I would also like to thank my friend and partner Andrew Butterfield for having introduced me to the extraordinary world of sculpture and for having helped me and participated in this exhibition.

Let us always remember that art is an anti-depressant that can certainly improve our daily life.

At the end of this brief introduction I would like to remember a person who is very dear to me, and who unfortunately recently passed away; I refer to Professor Luciano Bellosi, to whom I dedicate the present catalogue.

From the very beginning of my career, Luciano Bellosi was always kind and helpful towards me, giving me important advice that allowed me to improve and carry out my profession in the best way possible, and for this I shall always be extremely grateful to him.

The last time I saw him was in Florence. We dined together with my parents, Carl Strehlke, Moreno Bucci and Daniele Benati, a wonderful evening during which the Professor amused himself scrolling through the images in my iPhone and making attributions to the various works. An unforgettable evening that I shall always cherish in my heart. The qualities that have always struck me about this exceptional man, who left a fundamental mark in the history of Italian art, are the modesty and humility that only great people possess, and he was a undoubtedly a great man.

Grazie Professore!

Fabrizio Moretti

Contents

COLLECTING EARLY ITALIAN ART

The Beginnings

Dark clouds hung over Europe's skies and the European art heritage when Napoleon's troops swept throughout Europe and his gospel was the secularization, and thus the suppression, of ecclesiastical influence within political power. These world-shattering events had fatal consequences for Europe's artistic heritage in general, especially for the ecclesiastical libraries which were broken up and looted, and particularly for the numerous medieval and Renaissance altarpieces that were either still on the altars or otherwise stored, broken down and dismembered, in sacristies or elsewhere in the suppressed churches. This moment in history was fatal not only for the Italian religious houses but mainly for their rich cultural and artistic treasures, which were either destroyed due to the ignorance of the looting troops or, in more fortunate cases, removed from their original context and scattered all over the world in order to satisfy a growing market for medieval art. However, these years (1796-1799), critical as they were, coincided with a period of great interest in early Italian painting, when French and English connoisseurs joined their Italian colleagues in order to study early Italian art systematically, and publish various fundamental studies on this particular subject. In 1796 Luigi Lanzi brought out his *Storia pittorica dell'Italia*, and in the same years Séroux d'Agincourt (1730-1811) started preparing his *Histoire de l'Art par les monuments depuis sa decadence au 4ème siècle à son renouvellement au 16ème,* published in 1810-1823. Agincourt's book was to become a fundamental source of inspiration for the connoisseurship of early Italian art and the so-called "primitives".[1]

This fervent interest in early Italian art quickly swept through the English-speaking world, reaching first English and – after some initial hesitation – a few decades later also American enthusiasts and connoisseurs in this particular field. Among them was the sophisticated British amateur, connoisseur and curator, William Young Ottley (1771-1836), who was to furnish Agincourt's book with drawings after the major works of art discussed in this giant compendium of medieval and Renaissance art. At the time of Napoleon's presence in Italy, Ottley was on the spot and eager to acquire there the paintings and illuminated manuscripts that became easily available during the suppression of Italy's many important religious houses. He found himself in the company of other enthusiasts of the so-called "Italian Primitives", among them the French political entourage in Italy, including – to name but a few – Alexis-François Artaud de Montor (1772-1849), François Cacault (1743-1805) and the French Cardinal Fesch (1763-1839). As high-ranking French diplomats in Rome, they were easily able to come into possession of an enormous quantity of outstanding early Italian paintings and illuminations which in a very short space of time had become available to their illustrious circles and to collectors in general.

A few decades later, in addition to English collectors and experts such as Charles Fairfax Murray (1849-1919), the first American connoisseurs in this particular field of art – among them the Boston-born James Jackson Jarves (1818-1888) – also set out to conquer the rich artistic heritage of early Italian painting.

It was this generation of connoisseurs that was of fundamental importance in the creation of today's most distinguished collections of so-called Italian "primitives" in America and Great Britain. During his career Charles Fairfax Murray (1849-1919), a renowned English connoisseur, art dealer and advisor, who spent many years of his life in Florence (1876-1886), furnished the National Gallery in London and the Staatlichen Sammlungen in Berlin – to name just two of Europe's most prestigious museum institutions advised by him – with outstanding early Italian paintings, assembling at the same time an astonishing private collection of early Italian paintings, manuscripts, cuttings and single leaves. Rumour has it that during his innumerable visits to various Italian towns Fairfax Murray would frequently sit on a bench outside the local bars pounding the ground with a stick and shouting "Bring out your Madonnas! Two hundred lire!". This anecdote clearly implies a wealth of Italian art accessible in those years, and the easy and relatively inexpensive availability of such works for an eager and hungry art market.

After a certain initial diffidence towards early Italian art, the spark finally made it across the Atlantic to American collectors and found in James Jackson Jarves a highly refined collector

1. Luca di Tommè
Nativity
Florence, Carlo De Carlo collection

in this field. However, as is demonstrated by the intricate history of his collection and his long and frustrating attempts to house his sophisticated collection of gold-ground and Renaissance paintings, his enthusiasm for early Italian art was not immediately shared by American art institutions.[2]

In the early decades of the 20th century, under the "holy alliance" between Joseph Duveen (1869-1939) and Bernard Berenson (1865-1959), collecting early Italian art gradually became fashionable and chic. Berenson, born in Vilnius in Lithuania as Bernard Valvrojenski, and later brought up in Boston by his parents who took on the new name of Berenson, worked from the last decade of the 19th century as advisor to Isabella Stewart Gardner, a fervent admirer and collector of Italian art who had a special passion for Venetian painting. No wonder that it was to early Venetian art that Berenson dedicated his first research, publishing *The Venetian Painters of the Renaissance* in 1894, the first list of paintings by early Italian Renaissance painters ever published. This book was followed one year later by his study on Lorenzo Lotto. The rising star of connoisseurship was soon to become the chief advisor of the London and New York established *Duveen Bros.*, in those days headed by Joseph Duveen. This alliance would soon become of pivotal importance in the growing interest of American collectors in early Italian art, hence the forming and assembling of highly important American collections of early Italian painting. As already mentioned, Isabella Stewart Gardner's celebrated collection in Boston was the fruit of Berenson's efforts in the late years of the 19th century and the early years of the 20th century, and the "secret alliance" between Berenson and Duveen produced or at least contributed substantially toward the creation of the most remarkable American collections of early Italian art, such as the Frick collection in New York, the Huntington art collections and the National Gallery of Art in Washington. Joseph Duveen was also the driving force behind the assembling of the Robert Lehman collection, now at the Metropolitan Museum in New York.

These events contributed significantly to the passing on of this interest and joy in early Italian art to the present day, currently testified by the handsome collection of early Italian paintings owned by today's most distinguished American art dealer, Richard Feigen in New York.[3]

Of course, collecting early Italian art was actively pursued and in fashion throughout the centuries in the country where these wonderful paintings were originally conceived and created by the greatest artists and minds of the time: in Italy. Here the most eminent connoisseurs in the field contributed enormously to our knowledge of Italian painting, among them Roberto Longhi (1890-1970), a contemporary and lifetime rival of Bernard Berenson, and, in more recent times, in the second half of the 20th century, the late Federico Zeri (1929-1998); together with an illustrious generation of art dealers they have brought to our knowledge an immense number of highly significant Italian works of art. Florence had always been an important centre for the international art market, and in more recent times, and as far as gold-ground paintings and medieval and Renaissance art are concerned, it was dominated by an undisputed leader in matters of connoisseurship, the unforgettable Carlo De Carlo (1931-1999).

The present exhibition of a small, but wonderful selection of early Italian paintings and sculptures is dedicated to him, and consequently to a man, blessed with an admirable capacity for discernment that enabled him to judge immediately the artistic quality and cultural significance of a work of art. Who other than Carlo De Carlo could claim to be the modern heir of the great connoisseurs and amateurs of early Italian art of the early 19th century?

2., 3. Giotto
Saint Francis and *Saint John the Evangelist*
Florence, Cassa di Risparmio di Firenze collection

Carlo De Carlo – Connoisseur, Collector and Art Dealer

Carlo De Carlo was the prime example of a self-made man, who learned his lessons in Italian art not within the sterile confines of an Aula Magna in a prestigious university, but being a man blessed with an innate intuition for artistic quality, decided to go for his learning directly *ad fontes*, to the works of art themselves. Many stories have circulated about how Carlo De Carlo acquired his great knowledge of early Italian art and, in all honesty, no one really knows which of them are true or not. One thing is certain, however, and that is that even as a young man, during his numerous travels, he never missed an opportunity to visit the world's major art collections where he compared the works of art that he saw and reflected on the various artistic solutions chosen by different artists for similar artistic endeavours. It hardly comes as a surprise, therefore, that De Carlo would soon be making a living out of his vital interest in early Italian art. He married the daughter of a well-established Venetian art dealer and soon found his way into the fascinating world of antiquarians. From the time of his earliest experiences in this profession, he developed a particular predilection for early Tuscan painting and – it seems – particularly for the elegant and colourful world of Sienese art. What started off as a hobby soon turned into a vocation and a profitable business. This was also the right time to create a private collection which would later become a monument to his connoisseurship and professional talent. By selling paintings of lesser importance and at the same time buying other works of art of even higher quality, over many intense years as a distinguished art dealer De Carlo succeeded in refining and increasing his own collection. His interests as a passionate collector and as an antiquarian were inseparable, and produced up until his untimely death in December 1999 one of the most brilliant and outstanding collections of early Italian art put together in recent times. Fate had it that this monument of brilliant and sensitive connoisseurship would not endure and survive its creator, for the collection was sadly broken up soon after De Carlo's death and many of his treasures found their way into new collections, where they became the pride of their new owners.[4]

4. Bartolomeo Bulgarini
Virgin and Child with Saints
Asciano (Siena), Salini collection

Remembering De Carlo

My first personal contacts with De Carlo go back to the 1980s, when, on the occasion of the Florentine Art Fair, the *Biennale Internazionale dell'Antiquariato* – then still at Palazzo Strozzi – De Carlo allowed me to examine a Sienese gold-ground painting. Despite our radically different mentalities and background we gradually developed a mutual understanding which grew into a cordial and lasting friendship. De Carlo was a man of few words, who became vociferous only when he encountered disloyalty. I will never forget when during one of my visits I heard his thundering voice complaining over the phone about a disloyal agent who was apparently on the other end of the line. His movements were normally slow, even of a somewhat ghost-like nature, and his facial expression was generally controlled, thus Carlo De Carlo was of a bearing which, for a person unfamiliar with him, might have been perceived superficially as one of impenetrable distrust. This somewhat mysterious side of his character was immediately set aside when he examined and enjoyed one of his favourite works of art. When he met up with a colleague or friend of similar disposition towards early Italian art, sharing the pleasure of looking together at one or more of his latest discoveries, De Carlo's face lit up with passionate joy. I believe it was this innocent, child-like enjoyment of admiring a rediscovered masterpiece of early Italian art, common to both of us, that ultimately united us in an equally innocent and generally disinterested friendship. How could I ever forget one of those many phone calls from De Carlo that came right out of the blue?

"Freuler, I have to see you this evening. I have to show you something that you will like. Let's meet in that restaurant near Settignano." When the same evening I saw De Carlo entering the restaurant with a plastic shopping bag from an Italian supermarket and something well wrapped up in it, his eyes were sparkling. After dinner we drove to my place, and with his characteristic joyful smile he showed me a wonderful small Florentine triptych by Puccio di Simone and a predella panel with a Lorenzettian *Nativity* (Fig. 1) by Luca di Tommè which he carefully removed from its protective silk wrapping. I would later unite the small Sienese *Nativity* with its companion pieces and publish them in a study in which I offered a nearly complete reconstruction of a large early altarpiece by this Sienese master.[5] No different was the joy and pride in his face when he proudly showed me as a preview – probably one of many such previews – two small roundels with busts of saints by Giotto (Figg. 2, 3) – the two "biscottini" as he called them, which before my eyes he carefully freed from their silken veil. Who else among today's antiquarians could boast of having owned innumerable works by the likes of Giotto, Simone Martini,[6] the Lorenzettis, Giovanni Pisano, Ghiberti and by other similar exponents of early Italian art? At a certain point in his career, it almost seemed that it was no longer Carlo De Carlo who was looking for masterpieces, but, on the contrary, that these truly beautiful works found their way to him as if by their own accord, as if they had been inescapably attracted by a magnet, the charisma of this great connoisseur. Each of these stunning masterpieces, inexorably captured by the magnetism of his unmistakable eyes, stirred up his joy and his inner glow, especially when De Carlo shared them with his closest friends.

This honest open joy expressed by De Carlo should turn out to be a hint to a hidden aspect of his character, his talent as a comic that was to remain unrevealed to those who did not know him closely enough. I will never forget Carlo's hilarious imitation of a narrow-minded over-zealous Swiss customs officer in Zurich, who was to prepare for him the customs papers for a large predella by Angelo Puccinelli. Later on that same day I witnessed another unforgettably amusing scene typical of De Carlo. We had some hours left to spend together before he had to take the train to bring him and his predella back to Florence. After dinner we decided to go to a nearby cinema to watch one of those noisy war movies with Steven Seagal acting as a high-ranking Navy officer. Here we were, De Carlo, me and the four foot predella sitting in a Swiss movie theatre under the thundery noise of Seagal's *Under Siege*, and not even in the wildest dreams would anybody present in the movie theatre have imagined that wrapped in this long parcel, held by the eminent Florentine antiquarian in the second row, was a masterpiece of early Italian painting worthy of hanging on one of the walls of a prestigious museum.

Quality was a hallmark of a De Carlo painting. If anyone bought a painting from him he could be sure of owning a painting of considerable artistic significance and quality and, invariably, in good condition. They may not have been the absolute peak of his holdings, those he generally held back for his own collection, but as is demonstrated by the truly brilliant *Madonna and Child* from 1487 by Jacopo di Cione or the charming Sienese triptych by the Master of the Richardson Triptych in the present exhibition, they were always of outstanding quality. It hardly comes as a surprise that the most important works ever owned by De Carlo were among those he left behind after his untimely death. They were either bound to be sold in a near future or intended to be the absolute highlights of a private collection which unfortunately was not meant to survive its creator.[7] Some of De Carlo's most treasured works of art are today the pride of the most prestigious private collections. The stunningly elegant group of saints painted by the brothers Lippo and Tederigho Memmi and the early triptych by Pietro Lorenzetti both found their way into a private collection in Milan,[8] the large polyptych by Bartolomeo Bulgarini (Fig. 4) is now a highlight of the Salini collection near Asciano;[9] the triptych by the Master of San Lucchese figures among the works in the Pittas collection in Cyprus,[10] while the *Saint James the Greater* (Fig. 7) by Andrea di Nerio which was originally part of the same altarpiece as the *Saint Michael the Archangel* in the present exhibition today is owned by the Alana collection in Newark (Delaware).[11] The intriguing Duecento *Crucifixion* (Fig. 5) in a private collection,[12] the superb small Dominican *Maestà* by the Magdalen Master in private hands[13] as well as the small *Maestà* by Niccolò di Segna in the Pittas collection in Cyprus,[14] and another earlier *Maestà* in the Bargello in Florence by the Master of the Maestà Gondi, a follower of Duccio, the splendid *Blessing Christ* by Lorenzo Monaco (Fig. 6), now in the Galleria dell'Accademia in Florence[15] as well as with

5. Unknown Italian painter of the late 13th century (Bologna?)
Crucifixion
Private collection

the two already mentioned roundels by Giotto, now in the collection of the Cassa di Risparmio di Firenze in Florence (Figg. 2, 3),[16] all these paintings and numerous others not mentioned here represent the *crème de la crème* of early Italian art. The names of the artists who created these superb works read as a veritable "who's who" among the protagonists of early Italian painting. And the same is true for all the superb sculptures, carefully brought together by De Carlo. They bear witness to the art of the most exquisite early Italian sculptors such as Giovanni Pisano, Tino da Camaino, Nino Pisano, Lorenzo Ghiberti, Vecchietta, Donatello and Luca della Robbia, to name but a few, and unmistakably reveal De Carlo's particular sensitivity toward this artistic sector.[17]

If this small selection of outstanding works from the former Carlo De Carlo collection exhibited here stands as a modest, yet fitting homage to the most distinguished Italian art dealer of modern times, the other section of the exhibition embodying a small but worthy group of early Italian paintings and sculptures owned by the Moretti Gallery unequivocally shows that the collecting of early Italian art has retained all of its long-standing fascination and that the enduring beauty of these wonderful and inspiring works, produced centuries ago by the élite of Italian artists, has lost none of its allure on today's beholder. Thus the trade in early

6. Lorenzo Monaco
Blessing Christ
Florence, Galleria dell'Accademia

7. Andrea di Nerio
Saint James the Greater
Alana collection

Italian art continues to thrive, and, unlike other areas of collectionism, this particular field is not susceptible to fast changing fashions. In Fabrizio Moretti it has found a young and dynamic heir to De Carlo's connoisseurship. Being passionate, and, at the same time having the authority and connoisseurship befitting of an art historian, Moretti is a fortunate case for the modern trade in early Italian art, since he embodies many of the virtues that qualified his predecessors of the first generation in the early 19th century. They were not only passionate collectors and antiquarians, but also learned academics with a genuine interest in learning more about their *objets de désir*. These combined qualities are the prerequisites for the antiquarian's ultimate objective, that is, bringing all these magnificent works to light and creating the conditions that allow us a broader and deeper insight into art, thus building a bridge between the work of art and the beholder. If these requirements are met with in the present exhibition then all the efforts to make it happen have fulfilled their noblest purpose.

Gaudenz Freuler

1) For Séroux d'Agincourt see D. Mondini, *Mittelalter im Bild – Séroux d'Agincourt und die Kunsthistoriographie um 1800*, Zurich 2005; I. Mariani Miarelli, *Séroux d'Agincourt et l'Histoire de l'Art par les monuments. Riscoperta del medioevo, dibattito storiografico e riproduzione artistica tra fine XVIII e inizio XIX secolo*, Rome 2005.

2) For a concise summary of the history of the James Jackson Jarves collection see L. B. Kanter, *Italian Paintings in the Museum of Fine Arts Boston, Vol. 1, 13th-15th century*, Boston 1994, pp. 13-15.

3) L. Kanter, J. Marciari, *Italian Paintings from the Richard L. Feigen Collection*, New Haven/London 2010.

4) For a survey of the De Carlo collection see *Un tesoro rivelato. Capolavori dalla Collezione Carlo De Carlo*, eds. M. Scalini, A. Tartuferi, Florence 2001. Between 2000 and 2001, a large part of the Carlo De Carlo inventory was sold during several auctions held at Semenzato in Florence (18.-19.10.2000; 19.4.2001; 15.12.2001). Many other works of art of the De Carlo collection – some of them of high artistic value – have mysteriously disappeared and still wait to be traced.

5) G. Freuler, *L'eredità di Pietro Lorenzetti verso il 1350. Novità per Biagio di Goro, Niccolò di Sozzo e Luca di Tommè*, 'Nuovi Studi', II, 1997, pp. 15-32.

6) See the small panel with the bust of Saint Philip bought by De Carlo as lot 12 at the Christie's sale in New York on January 11th 1991 and lost since 1999.

7) See n. 4.

8) See the forthcoming catalogue of this collection curated by A. De Marchi to be published in 2012.

9) F. Mori, in *La Collezione Salini. Dipinti, sculture e oreficerie dei secoli XII, XIII, XIV e XV*, I, ed. L. Bellosi, Florence 2009, pp. 104-113.

10) S. G. Casu, *The Pittas Collection. Early Italian Paintings (1200-1530)*, Florence 2011, pp. 136-141.

11) A. Labriola, in *The Alana Collection. Italian Paintings from the 13th to 15th Century*, ed. M. Boskovits, Florence 2009, pp. 23-29.

12) L. Bellosi, in *Un tesoro rivelato* cit., pp. 18-19.

13) *Ibidem*, fig. on p. 32.

14) S. G. Casu, *The Pittas Collection* cit., pp. 180-183.

15) A. Tartuferi, in A. Tartuferi, D. Parenti, L. Monaco, *A Bridge from Giotto's heritage to the Renaissance*, exh. cat. (Florence, Galleria dell'Accademia, 9.5.-24.9.2006), Florence, pp. 167-171, cat. 23. A further work by the same master, an impressive large painted Crucifix dated on the back to 1397 (?), now lost, was also owned by Carlo De Carlo and was discussed by the present writer in the same catalogue (pp. 118-119, cat. 7).

16) L. Bellosi, *Due tavolette di Giotto*, in *Settanta studiosi italiani. Scritti per l'Istituto Germanico di Storia dell'Arte di Firenze*, Florence 1997, pp. 33-42.

17) More than fifty per cent of the splendid collection of Sienese sculptures in the Salini collection near Asciano, which includes wooden sculptures and marbles from the 13th to the 15th century were furnished by De Carlo. *La Collezione Salini* cit., vol. II.

The Middle Ages and Early Renaissance

Paintings and Sculptures from the Carlo De Carlo Collection
and other Provenance

Giovanni da Rimini

Rimini, documented from 1292 to 1336

1. Crucifix

Tempera on panel, 160.5 x 130 cm (63 $^1/_5$ x 51 $^1/_5$ in.)

Provenance:
Milan, Achillito Chiesa collection (?)
Jacques Goudstikker, Amsterdam, 1929
Requisitioned by the Nazi authorities, July 1940; recovered by the Allied forces, 1945; entrusted to the care of the Dutch government
Utrecht, Aartbisschoppelijk Museum, until 1987
Maastricht, Bonnefantenmuseum, until 1997
Rijswijk, Instituut Collectie Nederland
Returned to the heirs of Jacques Goudstikker, February 2006
London, Christie's, sale 5-6 July 2007, no. 7

Exhibitions:
Amsterdam, Rijksmuseum, *Tentoonstelling van Oude Kunst door de Vereeniging van handelaren in Oude Kunst in Nederland*, 1929, no. 115
Amsterdam, Stedelijk Museum, *Italiaansche kunst in Nederlands bezit*, 1934, no. 155
Rimini, Palazzo dell'Arengo, *La pittura riminese del Trecento*, 1935, no. 36.

At an unknown time in history the cross, destined to be placed against a screen inside a sacred building, was isolated. The panels at the extremities of the arms, containing the Mourners and the Blessing Christ, were eliminated, as was the lower end-piece and the large central panel against which the body of Christ, to below the knees, was supposed to stand out. A Bombelli photograph (ICCD, C 19408), taken when the painting was in Milan, presumably in the Chiesa collection,[1] shows, in addition to the deterioration of the painted surface, particularly the hair and beard, losses of colour near the left hand and the presence of invasive repaintings, in particular to the right and at the bottom of the hanging loincloth. Poorly restored, it figured at the great exhibition *La pittura riminese del Trecento* curated by Cesare Brandi in 1935, who as little as two years later lamented the "unsatisfactory incompletion" of the image caused by the curtailment of the original carpentry and by the forced shaping of the figure of Christ, noting that "its larva-like paleness, the tenuous anatomical notation anatomically standing out as pale on pale, has the effect of a song without accompaniment, a faint melody lacking any harmony". Although certainly unable to remedy these mutilations, the recent restoration, carried out in Florence by Paola Bracco, has restored order to the pictorial surface, removing the clumsy repaintings that concealed the structure of brushstrokes with which the flesh is rendered, even now admirable despite the overall impoverishment of the material, and restoring the original profile of the loincloth, which now hangs along the sides of the body in a much simpler way. Beneath the uniform dark film of colour that covered the cross, the texture of the wood has now re-emerged. As in other cases, the now almost black colour is the result of an alteration of blue. In the lower part of the side arms the restoration has brought out with greater clarity a subtle portion of the original gold background.

In the plate at the top of the cross, instead of the more frequent "INRI" (the abbreviation for "Iesus Nazarenus Rex Iudeorum"), the *titulus crucis* is formed by the Christogram "IC + XC", obtained from the first and last letter of the two words Jesus Christ in Greek characters (ΙΗΣΟΥΣ ΧΡΙΣΤΟΣ), with the final sigma written, as was usual in Oriental usage, in the lunar form that likens it to the Latin letter C.

Possibly belonging to the Chiesa collection in Milan, as the already mentioned photograph presumably taken during the 1920s by Girolamo Bombelli (Milan, 1882-1969) would appear to confirm, the painting was purchased by the Jewish merchant Jacques Goudstikker, who in 1929 presented it as the work of Giuliano da Rimini in an exhibition in his gallery in Amsterdam. In 1940, following the racial persecutions, his entire patrimony was requisitioned by the Nazis, while Goudstikker died accidentally when falling into the hold of the ship that was to take him to safety in England. Recovered by the Allied forces in 1945, his paintings were then entrusted to the care of the Dutch government and the *Crucifixion* under examination was exhibited first at the Aartbisschoppelijk Museum in Utrecht, then at the Bonnefantenmuseum in Maastricht and finally at the Instituut Collectie Nederland in Rijswijk (Fig. 1). In February 2006, at the end of a long dispute, the heirs obtained the restitution of this and other paintings formerly owned by Goudstikker and entrusted them to Christie's in London, which put them on auction in 2007.

In spite of its evident mutilation the painting very soon entered into the debate on the Riminese school. Initially believed to be a painting by Giuliano, in 1935 it was presented by Cesare Brandi at the exhibition *La pittura riminese del Trecento* as a work by Giovanni Baronzio, an artist under whose name two artists were at that time confused: the older *Johannes* who painted the cross of Mercatello, whose date was then read 1345 (Fig. 3), and the later Giovanni Baronzio, whose name and the date 1345 are read on a polyptych for-

1. Labels on the back of the work.

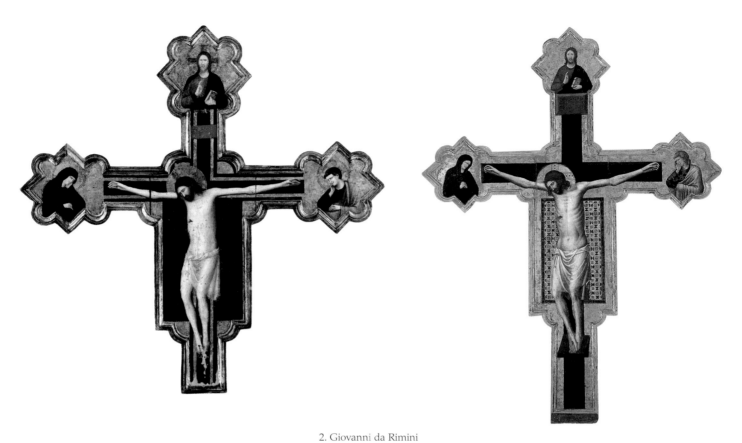

2. Giovanni da Rimini
'Diotallevi' Crucifix
Rimini, Museo della Città

3. Giovanni da Rimini
Crucifix
Mercatello sul Metauro (Pesaro-Urbino), San Francesco

merly at Macerata Feltria and now in the Galleria Nazionale delle Marche at Urbino. As well as with the cross of the Tempio Malatestiano – considered by him "the highest work that has remained of the Rimini school, fundamental and without any near comparison" for the way in which "the plasticism of Giotto" is "understood and transposed with the greatest stylistic freedom" (its full attribution to Giotto himself came with the *Giudizio sul Duecento* by Roberto Longhi, 1948) – in the catalogue Brandi compared it with the crosses of Mercatello and San Lorenzo a Talamello (the latter coming from the Augustinian complex of Poggiolo). Believed to be third in the series of crosses by Giovanni Baronzio, the Goudstikker cross was therefore dated between 1345 and 1350, although Brandi did not fail to draw attention to its blatantly archaic characteristics, such as the halo not standing out and not "in perspective", considering them "emblematic of a certain indifference with which Baronzio divulged and simplified the Riminese tradition".

In the third instalment of his long article on *La scuola di Rimini* (1937), Mario Salmi had established a connection with the cross of San Francesco at Sassoferrato, a work that would also be later variously discussed between *Johannes* and Giuliano, to whom it belongs. In that same year, 1937, Brandi returned to the problem and, accepting the distinction between the two Giovanni's proposed by Longhi in his university courses of 1934-1935, compared the Goudstikker cross to that formerly in the Diotallevi collection and now in the Museo della Città in Rimini, it too characterized by the presence of the *titulus* "IC + XC" (Fig. 2). Maurizio Bonicatti (1963) also supported a late dating, although he perceived, partly due to the presence of the Christogram in the plate, the tendency of the painter's "Byzantine background".

4. Giovanni da Rimini
'Diotallevi' Crucifix (detail)
Rimini, Museo della Città

5. Giovanni da Rimini
Crucifix (detail)
Talamello (Rimini), San Lorenzo

It was Carlo Volpe, in 1965, who grouped together the crosses of the older Giovanni, pointing out, albeit *in extremis* in a *post scriptum* at the end of his book, that the date on the Mercatello cross was not 1345, as had been accepted until then, but 1309 or 1314. The series, which started with the cross of Talamello, would therefore have culminated in that of Mercatello and then proceeded, between 1310 and 1320, with those of Goudstikker (then in the Aartbisschoppelijk Museum in Utrecht) and Diotallevi, the latter believed to be coeval with the frescoes of the chapel *a cornu epistulae* in Sant'Agostino at Rimini, formerly attributed to *Johannes* by Longhi. Again in 1979 Volpe would confirm this sequence, noting in the Diotallevi cross a "development […] in a more Gothic and certainly less archaic direction compared to that of Mercatello", for which, between the two options offered by the uncertain reading of the script, he resolutely opted in favour of the date 1309.

Subsequently, noting the echo offered by Giuliano da Rimini in the altar screen dated 1307 (Boston, Isabella Stuart Gardner Museum), the present writer (1986, I, p. 199) sustained an earlier date compared to the same Mercatello cross of the frescoes in the chapel *a cornu epistulae* in Sant'Agostino at Rimini and therefore also of the Diotallevi cross, which shows "in the body of Christ the same diaphanous beauty as the figures of Sant'Agostino, as if swathed in a tender luminescent cocoon, whereas the *Crucifixion* of Mercatello, by comparison, appears more evolved and complex in the exhibition of its culture components". The sequence proposed by Volpe was taken up again by Miklós Boskovits (1993), who claimed that the adoption of rectangular panels – rather than mixtilinear panels like those adopted

6. Giovanni da Rimini
Crucifix (detail)
Cat. 1

by Giotto starting precisely with the cross of Rimini – implied that the Talamello painting (Fig. 5) belonged to a much older phase compared to all the other crosses by Giovanni, deriving from a different prototype by Giotto on the type of the *Crucifixion* of Santa Maria Novella in Florence. While this indication was accepted by Alessandro Volpe,[2] a complete review of the sequence of crosses by Giovanni da Rimini has more recently been offered by Andrea De Marchi,[3] who – believing the choice of rectangular panels in the Talamello cross to be the result of a commission associated with more traditional preferences – has confirmed the early dating of the Diotallevi cross of the Museo della Città in Rimini, in which a clearly older stylistic and formal vocabulary is manifest. Even if reinterpreted in a naturalistic context based on the lesson learnt from Giotto, it is evident that in the Diotallevi cross the threefold knot of Christ's loincloth continues to allude to the *cingulum* of 13th-century crosses: a reference that tallies perfectly with an artist who, already working in 1292, must initially have expressed himself in accordance with the filo-Byzantine culture of those years, to then receive with enthusiasm the innovations introduced by Giotto in the course of his stay in Rimini some time before 1300.[4]

The elements contributing to the definition of the medieval cross are many, and should be assessed simultaneously. It was a type of object on which, given its importance in the sacred furnishing of the building, the liturgy imposed rules that were difficult to subvert. Besides the form of the carpentry, a detail which Carlo Volpe dwelt on insistently, and the naturalism conferred to the anatomy and the loincloth of Christ, another element that can be used to establish the chronological sequence of the crucifixes by Giovanni seems to me to be the particular *titulus crucis* adopted in the plate above the cross. Already in the cross of the Tempio Malatestiano in Rimini – the old San Francesco, of which he himself had decorated the apsidal part, presumably with stories of the titular saint – Giotto had affixed there the full Latin inscription "Iesus Nazarenus Rex Iudeorum", a choice that would be adopted by Giovanni in the crucifix of Mercatello (1309 or 1314), as well as by the mysterious 'Master of the choir of Sant'Agostino' (possibly *Zangolus*, brother of Giovanni and of Giuliano) in the cross that is still in Sant'Agostino in Rimini, datable, together with the frescoes of the choir, around 1315.[5] In the crosses of Diotallevi, Goudstikker and, possibly, Talamello, the Christogram "IC + XC" appears, which unmistakably refers to the figurative culture of the Eastern Church, promoted by the recovery of power by the Palaiologos dynasty that was well rooted in the Adriatic area at the end of the 13th century. This also seems to me an argument in favour of the early dating of the above-mentioned paintings compared to the Mercatello cross.

Supported by these initial assessments, it is posssible at this point to observe the cross presented here in a new light. It can be dated, in my view, to an intermediate phase between the Diotallevi cross and the cross of Mercatello. Besides the presence of the Christogram, the former is referred to in the subtle definition of the aristocratic face of Christ, still marked, on the top of the slightly aquiline nose, by a hint of 13th-century "forcella". A prelude to the latter, on the other hand, is the greater naturalism in the rendering of the ribcage and lower abdomen, described with very fine luminescent brushstrokes, as well as the beautiful loincloth, which now, following Giotto's example, swathes the flanks of Christ like a precious girdle. Since for the Diotallevi cross is hypothisizable a provenance from the chapel *a cornu epistulae* in Sant'Agostino, dedicated to the Madonna, for which a certain Umizolo di Neri in 1303 established a bequest that an image of the Madonna and Child and, significantly, a crucifix should be executed,[6] it would seem plausible to assign their execution to that year or just after. To the painting under examination belongs a slightly later date, some time between the 1305 and 1309 marked on the Mercatello cross; whereas subsequent to the latter appears to be the *Crucifixion* of Talamello, which, although adopting more antiquated solutions in the panels and, possibly, in the *titulus* (the problematic reading of the inscription plate, affected by an extensive loss of colour, advises a certain prudence on this) is striking for the greater regularization imposed on the squared features of Christ's face, with reference to choices that Giovanni himself, probably in collaboration with his brother Giuliano, would propose in the figures arranged at the sides of Christ in the *Last Judgement* that decorated the triumphal arch of Sant'Agostino (now Rimini, Museo della Città).

Despite its fragmentary condition, and although seldom taken into consideration by scholars (I myself, alarmed by its very poor state of preservation, was unwilling to request its loan for the exhibition on the *Trecento riminese* organized in Rimini in 1995), the cross presented here, following its recent restoration, can nonetheless be considered a benchmark in the production of Giovanni da Rimini, the oldest and noblest of the artists belonging to the school which flourished in the city following the sojourn of Giotto, miraculously able to combine the innovations proposed by the latter with the 13th-century "Palaiologos" substratum of his early artistic education.

Daniele Benati

1) W. Angelelli, A. De Marchi, *Pittura dal Duecento al primo Cinquecento nelle fotografie di Girolamo Bombelli*, Milan 1991, p. 162 no. 304.
2) A. Volpe, in *Il Trecento riminese. Maestri e botteghe tra Romagna e Marche*, exh. cat. (Rimini, Museo della Città, 20.8.1995-7.1.1996), ed. D. Benati, Milan 1995, p. 168; *idem*, *Giotto e i Riminesi*, Milan 2002, pp. 88-100.
3) A. De Marchi, *Una nuova tavola di Giuliano da Rimini*, 'L'Arco', 2003, 1, pp. 16-23.

4) A. Conti, in L. Castelfranchi Vegas, *L'arte medievale in Italia e nell'Ottocento europeo*, Milan 1993, p. 95; A. Volpe, *Neri da Rimini. Il Trecento riminese tra pittura e scultura*, exh. cat. (Rimini, Museo della Città, 2.4.-28.5.1995), Milan 1995, pp. 62-65.
5) D. Benati, in *Il Trecento riminese tra pittura e scultura* cit., p. 184.
6) *Idem*, in *ibidem*, p. 41.

Bibliography:

Catalogue des nouvelles acquisitions de la collection Goudstikker, Amsterdam, Jacques Goudstikker Gallery, 1929, no. 33

R. van Marle, *La pittura all'esposizione d'arte antica italiana di Amsterdam*, 'Bollettino d'arte', 28, 1934-1935, p. 446

C. Brandi, *La pittura riminese del Trecento*, exh. cat. (Rimini, Palazzo dell'Arengo, 20.6.-30.9.1935), Rimini 1935, p. 98 no. 36

M. Salmi, *La scuola di Rimini. III*, 'Rivista del R. Istituto Nazionale di Archeologia e Storia dell'arte', 5, 1935, pp. 115-116, fig. 27

C. Brandi, *Conclusioni su alcuni discussi problemi della pittura riminese del Trecento*, 'La critica d'arte', I, 1936, p. 237

Idem, *Giovanni da Rimini e Giovanni Baronzio*, 'La critica d'arte', II, 1937, pp. 196-197, pl. 137, fig. 4

M. Bonicatti, *Trecentisti riminesi. Sulla formazione della pittura riminese del '300*, Rome 1963, pp. 27, 30-32, 69-70 nos. 32, 75, fig. 32

C. Volpe, *La pittura riminese del Trecento*, Milan 1965, pp. 13-14, 16-17, 72 no. 15, fig. 35

B. Berenson, *Italian Pictures of the Renaissance. Central Italian and North Italian Schools*, London 1968, I, p. 363

D. Benati, C. Volpe, in *Pittura a Rimini tra Gotico e Manierismo*, exh. cat. (Rimini, Sala delle Colonne, August-October 1979), ed. C. Volpe, Rimini 1979, pp. 18, 20

C. Wright, *Paintings in Dutch Museums. An index of Oil Paintings in Public Collections in the Netherlands by Artists born before 1870*, London 1980, p. 141

C. Wiethoff, *De kunsthandelaar Jacques Goudstikker (1897-1940) en zijn betekenis voor het verzamelen van vroege italiaanse kunst in Nederland*, 'Kunsthistorisch Jaarboek', 32, 1981, pp. 256, 261, fig. 19

D. Benati, in *La pittura in Italia. Il Duecento e il Trecento*, ed. E. Castelnuovo, Milan 1986, II, p. 578

P. G. Pasini, *La pittura riminese del Trecento*, Rimini 1990, p. 63, repr.

W. Angelelli, A. De Marchi, *Pittura dal Duecento al primo Cinquecento nelle fotografie di Girolamo Bombelli*, Milan 1991, p. 162 no. 304

Old Master Paintings. An illustrated summary catalogue, Rijksdienst Beeldende Kunst (The Netherlandish Office for the Fine Arts), The Hague 1992, p. 106 no. 802, repr.

M. Boskovits, *Per la storia della pittura tra la Romagna e le Marche ai primi del '300. II*, 'Arte Cristiana', LXXXI, 756, 1993, p. 176 note 46

C. de Jongh-Janssen, D. van Wegen, *Catalogue of the Italian paintings in the Bonnefantenmuseum*, Maastricht 1995, pp. 52-53 no. 21

D. Benati, the entry *Giovanni da Rimini*, in *Enciclopedia dell'arte medievale*, ed. A. M. Romanini, VI, Rome 1995, p. 757

M. Minardi, the entry *Giovanni da Rimini*, in *Dizionario biografico degli italiani*, LVI, Rome 2001, p. 189

A. Volpe, *Giotto e i Riminesi*, Milan 2002, pp. 100, 170 note 41, repr. on p. 99

A. De Marchi, *Una nuova tavola di Giuliano da Rimini*, 'L'Arco', 2003, 1, p. 19 note 5

A. Marchi, in *Arte per mare. Dalmazia, Titano e Montefeltro dal primo Cristianesimo al Rinascimento*, exh. cat. (San Leo, San Marino, Museo di San Francesco, 22.7.-11.11.2007), eds. G. Gentili, A. Marchi, Milan 2007, p. 66

A. Tambini, the entry *Giovanni da Rimini*, in *SAUR. Allgemeines Künstlerlexikom*, 55, Leipzig 2007, p. 81.

Andrea di Nerio

Arezzo, documented between 1331 and 1369, already deceased in 1387

2. Saint Michael the Archangel

Tempera on panel, 62.3 x 32.3 cm (24 $^1/_2$ x 12 $^3/_4$ in.)

Provenance:
Paris, Baroni Gallery, in the 1950s
Florence, Carlo De Carlo collection
Florence, Lisa De Carlo collection

The panel represents Saint Michael the Archangel, who appears, as is usual, wearing armour, with a sword and shield, and with the slayed dragon at his feet, the symbol of victory over Satan and the rebel angels.

The Archangel is portrayed in full, in a frontal position, standing out against the gold, his feet resting on a ground painted in a colour that changes from red to pink. Michael's halo is formed of a finely-grained band, within which other leafy decorations can be discerned, freely executed by hand.[1] The panel, which can be admired for its excellent state of preservation, has a frame painted in imitation of a trilobate stone arch, which in turn is decorated with curling acanthus leaves in the pendentives. The support is made from a single piece of wood with a vertical grain, and has on the back the fragmentary representation of an angel executed in monochrome on a red background (Fig. 2).

This panel, well known to scholars, was part of a larger complex of which six fragments are known representing as many saints and similar in size: presumably, considering the information gleaned from the back (the vertical grain of the wood; the presence of a fragmentary representation of the Archangel Gabriel that must have been completed in other panels of the series; a bare strip of wood measuring twelve centimetres, implying the existence of a cross-piece), it must have been a large tabernacle with side panels[2] with a sculpted image in the centre.[3]

Of the series of saints, a *Saint James* (Alana collection, Fig. 4), a *Saint John the Evangelist*, a *Saint John the Baptist* (both formerly in the Baroni collection, Paris, Figg. 5-6), a *Bishop Saint*, possibly *Saint Donato* (at the Olomouc Castle Museum, in the Czech Republic, inv. O 380, Fig. 7) and a *Pope Saint*, possibly *Saint Gregory* (formerly in the Chalandon collection, at Parcieux, near Lyon, Fig. 8) have thus far emerged. The fact that the monochrome decorations of the pendentives are asymmetrical, at times matching the decoration of another panel in the series, suggests that the saints were originally arranged in pairs, while the probability that the representation of the Archangel was complete suggests that the rows with pairs of small saints were three in number[4] and not just two as has been otherwise supposed.[5] The *Saint Michael*, in particular, was placed next to the *Saint James* now part of the Alana collection, as is confirmed by the identical rendering of the colour of the background on which the saints are standing, the matching of the leaf decoration and also the presence, on the back of the Alana panel, of the remaining part of the face of the angel painted behind Saint Michael (Fig. 1).[6] Both panels, considering the leftward-looking gaze of Saint James, must

have been positioned on the right of the overall work of art, this being unanimously agreed upon by scholars.

Although in some of these panels the painter appears to have given great importance to the definition of shadows, based on a well-defined light source, we can't expect an extreme rigour in this attempt, in fact he failed to make the light source correspond in the two panels belonging to the same row. In the panel examined here the light is coming from the left, leaving in shadow the right side of the shield and the fingers of the Archangel's hand, which brandishes the sword, while in the *Saint James*, who was next to him, the light comes from the right, as is demonstrated by the thickening of colour on the left edge of the saint's mantle.

In 1956 four of these small panels were in the Baroni Gallery in Paris, where they were seen by Zeri, who, initially believing them to be a product of Pisan art of the Trecento, called the attention of the art scholar Enzo Carli on them. The latter actually included them in one of his books on Pisan painting of the Trecento with an attribution to a follower of the local artist Getto di Jacopo, a master close to Cecco di Pietro whose catalogue even today is limited to just two works: a small altarpiece with *Six saints and the Annunciation* (bearing the Del Testa and Da Caprona coats-of-arms, signed and dated 1391, and housed in the Museo Nazionale di San Matteo in Pisa) and a fresco with *Noli me tangere* (Palazzo Blu, Pisa).[7]

1. Andrea di Nerio
Saint James the Greater (back)
Alana collection

2. Andrea di Nerio
Saint Michael the Archangel (back)
Cat. 2

Returning to the issue several years later, Zeri added to the series the small panel with *Saint Gregory the Great* and, making good use of the pioneering research on Aretine medieval art carried out by Pier Paolo Donati and Luciano Bellosi,[8] attributed the paintings to an anonymous Aretine painter responsible also for the *Annunciation* which came to the Museo Diocesano of Arezzo from the destroyed church of San Marco at Murello, on which, during the restoration carried out in those very years the signature of Andrea di Nerio was found. In more recent times the biography of this artist has been enriched, partly as a result of new research on Spinello Aretino, of whom he must have been the first master. Documentary records on Andrea di Nerio emerging from archive investigations are very scarce: we know that in 1331 Andrea began to work as an independent master, in 1369 he is documented as still alive and he died in all probability around the middle of the 1380s. The *Annunciation* on panel, signed and today at the Museo Diocesano in Arezzo, must have been executed before 1364 – the date of another *Annunciation* frescoed in Santa Maria a Campogialli that seems to be a derivation from that by Andrea di Nerio[9] – and its chronology must have been towards the middle of the century.[10] Other works on panel grouped by critics under his name are the *Madonna and Child* formerly in the Harris collection (since 2007 at the Galleria Sarti in Paris),[11] two small panels with scenes from the life of John the Baptist housed at the Kunstmuseum in Bern that form a series with another small panel representing the *Birth of John the Baptist* at the Musée du Petit Palais in Avignon and with a fragment today at the Museo

3. Andrea di Nerio
Saint Michael the Archangel
Cat. 2

4. Andrea di Nerio
Saint James the Greater
Alana collection

Sacro del Cardinal Borgia of the Pinacoteca di Capodimonte,[12] and lastly an altarpiece comprising a series of scenes from the life of Jesus and Mary of which three fragments are today in a private collection in Munich.[13] Various frescoes are also attributed to him: the *Saints Francis and Dominic* painted on a column of the choir of the parish church of Arezzo have been attributed to an early phase of his artistic activity; more widely discussed is his later phase to which various fragments have been linked,[14] including the so-called *Puricelli Annunciation* today at the Museo Diocesano, the representation of Saint John Damascene on the right wall of the church of San Francesco, the frescoes in the parish church of Santa Maria at Sietina, and the *Stories of the Childhood of Jesus* in the church of San Lorenzo, works in which some scholars would prefer instead to identify the hand of artists influenced by Andrea though distinct from him.[15] A further problem is linked to the production of the so-called Master of the Vescovado – author, in 1334, of the frescoes of the Cappella Tarlati in the cathedral of Arezzo,[16] and a small corpus of works including various paintings on panel (like the six fragments with *Stories of Saint John the Evangelist and Saint John the Baptist* once part of the same dossal; the altarpiece with *Saints Dominic, Michael the Archangel and Paul* of the church of San Domenico in Arezzo, the *Triptych with Madonna and Saints* in the cathedral of Sant'Angelo in Vado) – who according to some scholars would be Andrea di Nerio himself in a still fairly early phase of his activity.[17]

In my view the *Saint Michael* and the small companion panels, as suggested by De Marchi

 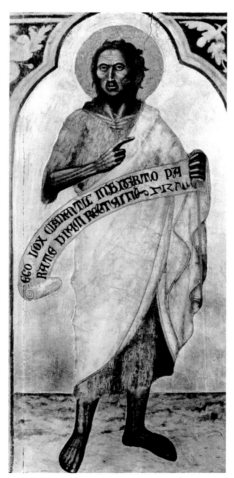

5. Andrea di Nerio
Saint John the Evangelist
Paris, Baroni collection (formerly)

6. Andrea di Nerio
Saint John the Baptist
Paris, Baroni collection (formerly)

and Bartalini,[18] belong to the early creative maturity of Andrea di Nerio, in the second half of the fourth decade of the Trecento,[19] that is the time when the Aretine painter showed an openness to the pointed and expressive style of Buonamico Buffalmacco, though it reveals above all a search for an essential and solemn monumentality. As some critics have already pointed out, these small panels have a connection above all with the *Madonna and Child* of the Sarti collection and like the latter show their affinity with the innovations of Florentine Giottesque painting.[20]

One of the major difficulties in the study of these panels, all of them apparently cut on various sides (preventing the observation of any possible marks left by hinges), is the impossibility of analyzing at first hand the entire known series. From the rather summary account of Federico Zeri, for example, it is impossible to understand if the other panels of the series also had on the back legible representations, which went, as would appear logical, to complete an Annunciation. The fragmentary figure of the Archangel that can be seen on the back of the *Saint James and Saint Michael* suggests that the Annunciation was characterized by the positioning of the Archangel on the right and the Virgin on the left. This was, as already noted by studies that have dealt with the question, a more unusual choice,[21] although it was certainly not unfamiliar to Florentine painters; Taddeo Gaddi, for example, had included it among the frescoes of the Cappella Baroncelli in Santa Croce and Andrea Orcagna had painted it in the panel of the Gerli collection in Milan. In the known portion of the Annun-

7. Andrea di Nerio
Saint Donato (?)
Czech Republic, Olomouc Castle Museum

8. Andrea di Nerio
Saint Gregory (?)
Parcieux (Lion), Chalandon collection

ciation plausibly represented on the back of these panels we are also struck by the presence of the leafy branch in the angel's hand, splaying in several directions, which would seem more similar to an olive frond rather than a palm, allowing us to exclude that the representation referred to a scene of the Annunciation of the Death of the Virgin.[22] On the other hand, as Andrea De Marchi has remarked (oral communication), this detail offers a possible *terminus post quem*, considering that this figurative idea was published for the first time in the celebrated altarpiece painted in 1333 for the altar of Sant'Ansano in the cathedral of Siena by Simone Martini and Lippo Memmi:[23] that Andrea di Nerio knew some derivation of it is not improbable, given that in Arezzo too there were traces of the work of the Memmi workshop.[24]

As mentioned at the beginning of the present text, the *Saint Michael* must plausibly have formed part of a large tabernacle with rectangular wings with a wooden sculpture inside, a good number of which must have existed in the Trecento especially between Umbria, the Marches and Abruzzo. We may imagine, to give an example among the various ones possible, a structure similar to the one visible until some years ago in the parish church of Pale, near Foligno.[25]

The series of saints chosen for the sides of this complex have not been clear enough for us to be able to trace their original location, allowing merely to surmise that it cannot have been a canonical series, constituted by all the doctors of the church, or all the evangelists, or all the apostles. Among those that have re-emerged, the representations of the bishop saint and the pope saint would seem to be connected with the Aretine area, where the bishop might allude to the patron of the city, Saint Donato,[26] and the pope Gregory would contribute to re-evoking Gregory X, who died in Arezzo in 1275 and for whom a monumental tomb had been installed in the Cathedral. Of the saints that have thus far emerged only the presence, one beside the other, of the two Johns (the Baptist and the Evangelist) would appear to be significant, in addition to the fact that the Baptist seems to have particular importance, holding a scroll with the entire quotation of the passage from Mark's Gospel (1:1-3): "Ego vox clamantis in deserto. Parate Viam Domini" followed by an "Inri" instead of the more usual "Ecce Agnus Dei" or the more essential "Ego vox clamantis in deserto", although this detail is, at the present time, too flimsy for any firm conclusions to be drawn.

Linda Pisani

1) This decorative detail would also imply a fairly early dating, around 1335-1340, of the panel with Saint Michael, as will be argued further on in the text.

2) As proposed by F. Zeri, *Un problema del Trecento aretino*, in *Diari di Lavoro 1*, Bergamo 1971, pp. 28-32; republished in *idem, Giorno per giorno nella pittura. Scritti sull'arte toscana dal Trecento al Cinquecento*, Turin 1992, pp. 39-40.

3) As suggested by A. De Marchi, *Rari dipinti di antichi maestri*, Venice, Semenzato, 17.4.2005, pp. 98-101. The alternative, several times ventilated in scholarly studies (A. Lenza, *Andrea di Nerio*, in *Le opere del ricordo. Opere d'arte dal XIV al XVI secolo appartenute a Carlo De Carlo, presentate dalla figlia Lisa*, ed. A. Tartuferi, Florence 2007, pp. 14-19; A. Labriola, *Andrea di Nerio*, in *The Alana Collection. Italian Paintings from the 13th to 15th century*, ed. M. Boskovits, Florence 2009, pp. 23-29), is that it was a large triptych, representing, at the sides, various saints, arranged in more than one row, and, in the centre, a painted image of the Madonna and Child of larger dimensions. In any case, as underlined by A. De Marchi (*Andrea di Nerio. Vierge à l'Enfant*, in *Entre Tradition et modernité. Peinture italienne des XIVe et XVe siècles*, Paris 2008, pp. 24-32), it could not have been a dossal of the type paint-

ed by the Master of Saint Francis around 1270 or by Giuliano da Rimini in 1308, examples cited by A. Lenza (*Andrea di Nerio* cit.), which are constructed with horizontal pieces of wood.

4) A. De Marchi, *Rari dipinti di antichi maestri* cit.; *idem, Andrea di Nerio. Vierge à l'Enfant* cit.

5) F. Zeri, *Un problema del Trecento* cit.; A. Lenza, *Andrea di Nerio* cit.; A. Labriola, *Andrea di Nerio* cit.

6) Images of the two backs of the *Saint Michael* and *Saint James* have been usefully published and commented on by A. Labriola (*Andrea di Nerio* cit.). The same scholar, noting the presence of the diadem on the figure's forehead, definitively confirms his identification as the Archangel Gabriel. Andrea De Marchi too, who had previously thought of the possibility of seeing there the representation of a martyr saint, is now convinced that it is rather an Annunciation with the angel coming from the right (oral communication) and has suggested to me the possibility of inferring from it a useful chronological indication (see text).

7) For a recent summary on Getto di Jacopo cf. *Cecco di Pietro e i fondi oro di Palazzo Blu*, exh. cat. (Pisa 2011), ed. L. Pisani, Florence 2011, pp. 8-21.

8) F. Zeri, *Un problema del Trecento* cit; L. Bellosi, *Da Spinello Aretino a Lorenzo Monaco*, 'Paragone', XVI, 187, pp. 18-43; P. Donati, *Contributo a Spinello Aretino e alla sua scuola*, 'Antichità Viva', III, 1964, 4, pp. 11-24; P. Donati, *Per la pittura aretina del Trecento II*, 'Paragone', XIX, 1968, 215, pp. 22-39; P. Donati, *Per la pittura aretina del Trecento II*, 'Paragone', XIX, 1968, 221, pp. 10-21; P. Donati, *Per la pittura aretina del Trecento III*, 'Paragone', XXI, 1970, 241, pp. 3-11.

9) As Weppelmann mentions, offering a useful summary of the life and work of Andrea di Nerio (S. Weppelmann, *Spinello Aretino e la pittura del Trecento in Toscana*, Florence 2011, pp. 45-46).

10) R. Bartalini, *Da Gregorio e Donato ad Andrea di Nerio: vicende della pittura aretina del Trecento*, in *Arte in terra d'Arezzo*, Florence 2005, pp. 28-40; A. De Marchi, *Rari dipinti di antichi maestri* cit.

11) For which cf. A. De Marchi, *Andrea di Nerio. Vierge à l'Enfant* cit.

12) On which cf. G. Freuler, *Andrea di Nerio*, in *Manifestatori delle cose miracolose. Arte italiana del Trecento e del Quattrocento da collezioni in Svizzera e nel Liechtenstein*, exh. cat. (Thyssen Bornemisza Foundation 1991), Einsiedeln 1991, pp. 189-190.

13) For these fragments cf. S. Weppelmann, *Spinello Aretino* cit., p. 84 note 13.

14) S. Weppelmann, *Andrea di Nerio o Spinello aretino?*, 'Nuovi Studi', 4, 1999, pp. 5-16; *idem*, *Spinello Aretino* cit.

15) R. Bartalini, *Da Gregorio e Donato ad Andrea di Nerio* cit. For the identification of Saint John Damascene see I. Droandi, *Tracce di un matrimonio nella pittura aretina del Trecento*, 'Annali aretini', XIII, 2005, p. 146.

16) For which cf. *idem*, *I Tarlati. Il "Maestro del Vescovado" e la pittura aretina della prima metà del Trecento*, 'Prospettiva', 83-84, 1996-1997, pp. 30-56.

17) This opinion is shared by M. Boskovits (*Marginalia su Buf-falmacco e la pittura aretina del primo Trecento*, 'Arte Cristiana', LXXXVI, 1998, 786, pp. 165-176) and A. De Marchi (*Maestro del Vescovado [Andrea di Nerio?]*, catalogue entry, now being published).

18) A. De Marchi, *Andrea di Nerio*, in *Eredi Carlo De Carlo, part V*, Florence, Semenzato auction, 11.6.2003, lots 11-12; A. De Marchi, *Rari dipinti di antichi maestri* cit.; A. De Marchi, *Andrea di Nerio. Vierge à l'Enfant* cit.; and R. Bartalini, *Da Gregorio e Donato ad Andrea di Nerio* cit.

19) Of a different opinion M. Boskovits, *Appunti su un libro recente*, 'Antichità Viva', X, 1971, 5, pp. 3-15 (who proposes the decade 1355-1365), and A. Labriola, *Andrea di Nerio* cit. (who suggests an execution during the 5-year period 1355-1360).

20) The name of Maso di Banco has several times been advanced as a point of reference for this phase of Andrea di Nerio's career. On this M. Boskovits (*Marginalia* cit.) has expressed skepticism, more recently echoed by A. De Marchi (*Maestro del Vescovado* cit.) who prefers to lend credibility to the influence exerted by Giotto's mature production, at the time of the Cappella Bardi.

21) A. Lenza, *Andrea di Nerio* cit.; A. Labriola, *Andrea di Nerio* cit.

22) Suggested, as a remote possibility, by A. Labriola, *Andrea di Nerio* cit. For an example of this iconography see the *Annunciation of the Death of the Virgin* frescoed by Taddeo di Bartolo in the end wall of the Cappella Sardi in the sacristy of the Pisan church of San Francesco, where, in effect, the announcement comes from the right, but the angel is holding a palm leaf. The source for this scene is a passage of the *Legenda Aurea* by Jacopo da Varagine, which reads "Ecco ch'abbo recato a te, Madonna uno ramo di palma del Paradiso, la quale tu comanderai che si porti innanzi al cataletto quando tu sarai al terzo die ricevuta del corpo, però che 'l

tuo figliuolo aspetta te, madre di reverentia" (cf. G. Solberg, *Taddeo di Bartolo: His life and Work* [New York University 1991], Ann Arbor 1991, I, pp. 746-747).

23) In the *Annunciation* by Simone the olive branch is fruit-bearing and should be interpreted not only as a sign of peace, but also as a direct reference to the symbolism of the Virgin (for this interpretation, based on the Holy Scriptures, cf. I. Hueck, *L'Annunciazione e Santi di Simone Martini e Lippo Memmi*, in *Simone Martini e l'Annunciazione degli Uffizi*, ed. A. Cecchi, Milan 2001, pp. 11-34). On the importance of the panel painted by Simone and Lippo Memmi, see the thorough analysis by A. De Marchi, *La parte di Simone e la parte di Lippo*, 'Nuovi Studi', XI, 2007, 12, pp. 5-24.

24) I refer to the four evangelists frescoed on the ceiling of the Dragomanni chapel in the church of San Domenico in Arezzo, reproduced as the work of 'Barna' by M. Salmi, *San Domenico e San Francesco di Arezzo*, Florence 1951, pp. 15-16,

fig. 13, for which Aldo Galli (*Appunti per la scultura gotica ad Arezzo*, in *Arte in terra d'Arezzo*, Florence 2005, pp. 113-137, particularly pp. 128-130 and 135 note 84) and A. Labriola (*Andrea di Nerio* cit., p. 26) advance the name of Lippo Memmi. In this case however, as underlined by Galli, they were later frescoes and could hardly have influenced Andrea di Nerio at the time of these saints.

25) See the image of it, complete with painted wings (later stolen) and the commentary, in C. Fratini, *Scultura lignea policroma e pittura nell'"Umbria" del Trecento*, 'Commentari d'Arte', IV, 1998, pp. 41-42, fig. 7. Observing this structure, the wings appear noticeably each made of two different axes: if this had been the case also in the work of Andrea di Nerio it would well explain the presence, at least at the top, of a reinforcing cross-piece.

26) R. Bartalini, *Da Gregorio e Donato ad Andrea di Nerio* cit.

Bibliography:

E. Carli, *Pittura pisana del Trecento. La seconda metà del secolo*, Milan 1961, II, p. 69

M. Boskovits, *Appunti su un libro recente*, 'Antichità Viva', X, 1971, 5, pp. 6, 11 note 14 and 12 note 18

F. Zeri, *Un problema del Trecento aretino*, in *Diari di Lavoro 1*, Bergamo 1971, pp. 28-29; republished in *idem, Giorno per giorno nella pittura. Scritti sull'arte toscana dal Trecento al Cinquecento*, Turin 1992, pp. 39-40 and fig. 47

L. Bellosi, *Buffalmacco e il trionfo della morte*, Turin 1974, pp. 55-56 note 7

A. M. Maetzke, *Dipinti, Sculture e arti minori*, in *Arte nell'Aretino. Recuperi e restauri dal 1968 al 1974*, exh. cat. (Arezzo 1974-1975), eds. L. G. Boccia, C. Corsi, A. M. Maeztke, A. Secchi, Florence 1974, pp. 54, 57

C. Volpe, *Un polittico integrato di Spinello (e alcune osservazioni su Maso)*, 'Paragone', XXX, 1979, 349, pp. 31, 34

A. De Marchi, *La mostra di pittura italiana del Gotico e del Rinascimento a Praga*, 'Prospettiva', 45, 1986, p. 75

S. Ricci, in *La Pittura in Italia*, II, Milan 1986, pp. 552, 618

O. Pujmanova, *Italské gotické a renesancnì obrazy v ceskoslovensk ch sbìrkàch*, exh. cat. (Palazzo Sternberk, Prague 1986), Prague 1986, cat. 2, pp. 37-39

L. Bellosi, see *Andrea di Nerio*, in *Allgemeines Künstler Lexikon*, III, München-Leipzig 1992, p. 545

R. Bartalini, *I Tarlati. Il "Maestro del Vescovado" e la pittura aretina della prima metà del Trecento*, 'Prospettiva', 83-84, 1996-1997, p. 54 note 38

O. Pujmanova, *Arte rinascimentale italiana nelle collezioni ceche. Pitture e sculture*, Prague 1997, cat. 5, p. 24

S. Weppelmann, *Andrea di Nerio o Spinello aretino?*, 'Nuovi Studi' 4, 1999, pp. 7, 12, 16 note 15

I. Droandi, *Questioni di pittura aretina del Trecento*, 'Annali aretini', 2000-2001, pp. 365, 371 note 77, 380

A. De Marchi, *Andrea di Nerio*, in *Eredi Carlo De Carlo, part V*, Florence, Semenzato auction 11.6.2003, lots 11-12

L. Bellosi, *Riconsiderazione sull'opera giovanile di Spinello e qualche cenno alla sua attività giovanile più tarda*, in *Arte in terra d'Arezzo*, Florence 2005, p. 98

R. Bartalini, *Da Gregorio e Donato ad Andrea di Nerio: vicende della pittura aretina del Trecento*, in *Arte in terra d'Arezzo*, Florence 2005, pp. 31-32 and 34 note 77

A. De Marchi, *Rari dipinti di antichi maestri*, Venice, Semenzato, 17.4.2005, pp. 98-100

A. Lenza, *Andrea di Nerio*, in *Le opere del ricordo. Opere d'arte dal XIV al XVI secolo appartenute a Carlo De Carlo, presentate dalla figlia Lisa*, ed. A. Tartuferi, Florence 2007, pp. 14-19

A. De Marchi, *Andrea di Nerio. Vierge à l'Enfant*, in *Entre Tradition et modernité. Peinture italienne des XIVe et XVe siècles*, Paris 2008, pp. 24-32

A. Labriola, *Andrea di Nerio*, in *The Alana Collection. Italian Paintings from the 13th to 15th century*, ed. M. Boskovits, Florence 2009, pp. 24-29, fig. 5e

S. Weppelmann, *Spinello Aretino e la pittura del Trecento in Toscana*, Florence 2011, p. 84 note 12.

Andrea Bonaiuti

Florence, documented from 1346, died 1379

3. Crucifixion

Tempera on panel, 27.5 x 11 cm (10 $^4/_5$ x 4 $^1/_3$ in.)

Provenance:
London, private collection

The scene of the Crucifixion, probably due to the very small size of the painting, is described with extreme essentiality, and limited only to the main figures: Jesus, the Virgin and Saint John the Evangelist wearing a green tunic covered by a yellow-lined pink mantle instead of the traditional blue tunic and pink mantle.

In all probability the small panel originally constituted the panel of a portable triptych destined for private devotion. In the cusp there may have been a representation of the Angel of the Annunciation or the Virgin Annunciate, in the central compartment the Madonna and Child with saints or the less usual scene of the Coronation of the Virgin, while in the other panel one or more saints or an episode of the life of Jesus, in line with the most common typologies of the devotional tabernacles of the time (for example the triptych by Bernardo Daddi of the Lindenau-Museum of Altenburg[1] and the one by Bonaiuti in a Bolognese private collection,[2] or the one by Puccio di Simone with the *Coronation*[3]).

The painting, unpublished as far as the present writer is aware, recently appeared on the English antique market with the correct attribution to Andrea Bonaiuti, confirmed on the basis of photos also by Miklós Boskovits (oral communication) and Johannes Tripps (oral communication).

The scarcity of records on the activity of this painter makes it difficult to compile a chronological table of his works; in fact, the year of his enrolment in the Guild of Physicians and Apothecaries, in 1346, and the time of his first known commission, on 30 December 1365, when he was charged with the decoration over the next two years of the chapter-house of the Dominican convent of Santa Maria Novella, are separated by a period of almost twenty years. Andrea Bonaiuti probably received his artistic training under Andrea di Cione, as is revealed by a group of small works destined for private devotion and datable between the fifth and sixth decade of the 14th century (the *Madonna and Child with Saints* formerly in a private collection in Cologne, a dismembered triptych – Fig. 1 – split between the Statens Museum for Kunst of Copenhagen and the Museum of Fine Arts of Houston, Texas, another fragmentary triptych divided between the Berenson Foundation at Settignano, near Florence, and the Museo Nazionale di Capodimonte in Naples, and the *Saint John the Baptist and Saint James* formerly in Brussels, Stoclet collection[4]): these are characterized by a tendentially two-dimensional vision and by strong chiaroscuro contrasts that accentuate the anatomical structure of the bodies. These features also appear in the panel presented here: the emaciated body of Christ is strongly underlined by soft, fused shadows that emphasize the muscles of the ribcage and above all those of the almost skeletal arms, which are in tension due to his position on the Cross, particulars that reveal the descriptive nature and vivid

1. Andrea Bonaiuti
Reconstruction of a triptych
Copenhagen, Statens Museum for Kunst (central)
Houston (Texas), Museum of Fine Arts (laterals)

interest in detail typical of all his artistic production. Another common element in these works, and indicative of the artist's probable training under Andrea di Cione, is the expressive severity of the figures; indeed, the two mourners witness the scene in silence and the immobility of the composition is barely ruffled by the blessing gesture of Saint John. Also noteworthy, despite its small size, is the search for effects of preciousness, typical of the early small-format paintings by Andrea and Orcagnesque painters active in the sixth decade of the 14th century and evident in the striking decorative band running along the inner edges where the very common punched motif of the six-petalled rosette has been used. The stiff folds of the clothes and the incised and simplified outline are still far from the compositional refinements that would characterize the works of his mature phase, like the two precious small panels with Saint Agnes and Saint Domitilla (Florence, Galleria dell'Accademia; Fig. 2) datable towards the middle of the 1360s and the apex of his artistic production; on the basis of these considerations, therefore, it is possible to hypothesize for the *Crucifixion* a date near the beginning of Andrea's stylistic development, around 1350, and therefore consider it one of his very earliest works.

Alberto Lenza

2. Andrea Bonaiuti
Saint Agnes and Saint Domitilla
Florence, Galleria dell'Accademia

1) M. Boskovits, *A Critical and Historical Corpus of Florentine Painting*, Sec. III, Vol. III, *The works of Bernardo Daddi*, Florence 1989, pl. XII.
2) J. Tripps, *A Critical and Historical Corpus of Florentine Painting*, Sec. IV, Vol. VII (Part I), *Tendencies of Gothic in Florence: Andrea Bonaiuti*, Florence 1996, pl. XXI.

3) A. Labriola, in *Da Bernardo Daddi al Beato Angelico a Botticelli. Dipinti fiorentini del Lindenau Museum in Altenburg*, ed. M. Boskovits with the assistance of D. Parenti, Florence 2005, pp. 193-194.
4) J. Tripps, *A Critical and Historical Corpus* cit., respectively plates I, II, III and IV.

NICCOLÒ DI BUONACCORSO

Siena, documented 1372-1388

4. Crucifixion

Tempera on panel, 45.6 x 21.3 cm (18 x 8 $^2/_5$ in.)

Provenance:
London, private collection

The present panel of small dimensions with the expressive yet composed representation of the Crucifixion is an outstanding example of the Sienese production of small-scale altar-pieces or panels for personal devotion which in Siena, after the second plague of 1363, became increasingly popular. In those years and later, specialized workshops responded to the great demand for such products. The workshops of masters such as that of the so-called Master of the Pietà and, most prominently, the workshop of Niccolò di Buonaccorso, to name but two, were, it seems, the most highly sought-after enterprises for the production of such objects, which were characterized by precious decoration and highly developed spatial effects.

As will be argued, it is to Niccolò di Buonaccorso that we should attribute this fine and hitherto little-known painting.

The stylistic formulas and typology visible in this panel are clearly reminiscent of the Sienese painters in the following of Simone Martini, such as Lippo Memmi and the Master of the Palazzo Venezia Madonna.

This is true not only for the Virgin mourning over her son, which recalls models seen in the New Testament cycle that Lippo Memmi and his workshop (including his brother Tederigho Memmi) had painted in the collegiata of San Gimignano around 1340, but also for the figure of Christ on the Cross, which recalls that of the *Crucifixions* by Lippo Memmi in the Louvre (Fig. 1) and by a later follower of Simone Martini from the Phillips collection in Montreal, now in deposit in the Fogg Art Museum in Cambridge (Mass.).

The compositional concept of the present *Crucifixion* is undoubtedly a refined – as we shall discuss – earlier variation of the one that Niccolò di Buonaccorso painted on the right panel of the diptych in the Galleria Nazionale dell'Aquila (Fig. 2), which is rendered with a more emotional tone. In both pictures Mary Magdalen is given a prominent and privileged role, being shown turned frontally toward the beholder, facing him with grief, inviting him at the same time empathically to be a part of the group of mourners under the Cross, hence drawing him into the picture. This is just one of the many elements characteristic of Niccolò di Buonaccorso's remarkable skill in creating a drama in his pictures that aimed to arouse the beholder's contemplative sympathy in the scene represented. This aspect in painting was the functional kernel of a picture of private devotion and Niccolò di Buonaccorso was a master in the pictorial creation of empathy. If in the L'Aquila *Crucifixion* he represented his story with a greater emotional charge and more animated action (Saint John), here the calm and composed atmosphere induces the beholder to join in the absorbed meditation expressed by Christ's mother and his favourite disciple John. The only person who speaks directly to the

1. Lippo Memmi
Crucifixion
Paris, Musée du Louvre

viewer is the slender figure of Mary Magdalen, who stridently cries out her grief to us. As she grasps the foot of the Cross with her left hand her red coat falls to the ground, the folds creating a dramatic series of rippling waves. The other mourners are represented in a state of composed grieving, absorbed as they are in silent meditation, which in the case of the Virgin is emphasized by the tranquil gesture of her head resting on her left hand.

The astonishing invention of Mary Magdalen's mantle falling to the ground, which makes it look as if the waves of a sea drenched in blood had broken on the shores, is repeated in a less spectacular way in Niccolò da Buonaccorso's panel in L'Aquila. The remarkably dynamic effect of these folds evidently aims to subtly underline the saint's inner turmoil, which in this manner finds an appropriate aesthetic echo. Some decades later this dramaturgic detail must have impressed Andrea di Bartolo, who included it in a similar context in his triptych no. 153 in the Pinacoteca Nazionale di Siena.

Such finesse in the art of dramaturgy can only be credited to an artist of supreme ability and

2. Niccolò di Buonaccorso
Mystic Marriage of Saint Catherine and *Crucifixion*
L'Aquila, Museo Nazionale

it was presumably this very skill that made Niccolò di Buonaccorso one of Siena's most sought-after painters in the field of paintings for private devotion.

The attribution of the present painting to Niccolò di Buonaccorso is not as obvious as for most of his other paintings and therefore requires some further explanation.

The style of Niccolò di Buonaccorso's paintings is generally uniform, changing little during the course of his artistic activity. Combined with the scarcity of biographical information, this aspect of his art makes it difficult to present a reliable chronological assessment of his career. The only two firm chronological references during the period of his artistic production, which was cut short by a sudden and presumably early death in 1388, relate to his later years of activity and concern the dated (1385) Biccherna with an Allegory of the "Government Restored Restraining the Citizen" in the Siena State Archive[1] and the panels from the dated (1387) altarpiece of Santa Margherita at Costalpino.[2]

The paintings from his later years of activity clearly reveal the inspiration he drew from the art of the then leading Sienese painter Bartolo di Fredi. His observance for Bartolo was carried to such an extent that at times his paintings became hardly distinguishable from those by the elder painter.

Despite the clear stylistic affinities with the bulk of Niccolò di Buonaccorso's paintings, presumably painted in the 1370s which was the most important period of his activity, our painting differs in style not only from that of the main body of our artist's oeuvre but also – even more radically – from his later paintings under the influence of Bartolo di Fredi.

The figures in our *Crucifixion* are not yet formed according to the artist's habitual formulas, which in some cases make the figures resemble mask-like beings. On the other hand Christ's finely drawn features and thin elongated nose and Mary Magdalen's slender frontal

3. Naddo Ceccarelli
Crucifixion
© Cambridge, Fitzwilliam Museum

face seem to belong to the same family as the many figures appearing in two wings painted in grisaille in the Alte Pinakothek in Munich, which with good reason have been attributed to Niccolò di Buonaccorso by Miklós Boskovits and more recently by Pia Palladino.[3]
Furthermore, the rounded face of the seraphim hovering on the lower right side around the
cross, especially his lively and characteristically rounded eyes perfectly compares to the features of the little seraphim in Niccolò di Buonaccorso's *Annunciation* in the Wadsworth
Atheneum in Hartford.
Pia Palladino, who in 1997 undertook the first successful attempt to reconstruct a chronology for Niccolò di Buonaccorso's oeuvre, convincingly placed the Munich panels at the
beginning of the painter's activity, which she believed must have started around 1370.[4]

If it is true that Niccolò di Buonaccorso was indeed the son of the painter Buonaccorso di Pace and may have been born around 1348 or thereabouts, and considering that in the supplement added in the years between 1378 and 1386 to the painter's guild in Siena of 1356 Niccolò di Buonaccorso is mentioned after Andrea Vanni, we have good reason to believe that the artist's career began slightly earlier than envisaged by Palladino, therefore in the later years of the 1360s.

The absence in our painting of the rather stylized formulas so characteristic of his hitherto known artistic production, as well as the lack of ornamental features which increasingly find their way into the artist's oeuvre, make it highly probable that this fine *Crucifixion* dates from the very beginning of Niccolò di Buonaccorso's artistic career, and a date around 1368 would seem highly probable. A comparison with the *Crucifixion* assigned to Naddo Ceccarelli in the Fitzwilliam Museum in Cambridge, no. 588 (Fig. 3), clearly reveals the artistic sources for the emerging Niccolò di Buonaccorso. What clearly emerges from this comparison is that the painting in question is based on carefully observed earlier models found among the paintings of the late followers of Simone Martini, particularly Naddo Ceccarelli, as well as in the works of Lippo and Tederigho Memmi. Certain abstractions in the facial features which share simplified formulas not uncommon to Andrea Vanni, are drawn directly from the repertoire of artists of Simone Martini's entourage such as the Memmi brothers (e.g. the *Crucifixion* in the Louvre) and the Master of the Palazzo Venezia Madonna. After his début within the milieu of the then late followers of Simone Martini, Niccolò di Buonaccorso soon directed his art towards an increasingly precious miniaturist quality of execution, introducing an application of brilliant 'sgraffito' decoration and rich gilding of the frames. The rediscovery of this fine panel and its attribution to Niccolò di Buonaccorso helps us to assess the earlier phase of his artistic activity, which seems to have been influenced initially by the late followers of Simone Martini and the Memmi brothers, and more specifically by painters like the Master of the Palazzo Venezia Madonna and Naddo Ceccarelli, and later also by Jacopo di Mino del Pellicciaio, who seems to have suggested to him a style that was a stylistic synopsis of artistic formulas proposed by two of the most important currents in Sienese painting, those of Simone Martini and the Lorenzetti brothers.

Gaudenz Freuler

1) J. Pope Hennessy, L. B. Kanter, *Italian Painting in the Lehman Collection*, New York 1987, p. 33.

2) M. Boskovits, *Su Niccolò di Buonaccorso, Benedetto di Bindo e la pittura di primo Quattrocento*, 'Paragone', XXXI, 1980, 359-361, pp. 4-5.

3) *Ibidem*; P. Palladino, *Art and Devotion in Siena after 1350. Luca di Tommè and Niccolò di Buonaccorso*, San Diego (Cal.) 1997, p. 46 ff.

4) P. Palladino, *Art and Devotion* cit., p. 54.

SIMONE DI FILIPPO, CALLED 'DEI CROCIFISSI'

Bologna, documented from 1354, died 1399

5. Virgin and Child between Saints John the Baptist and Bartholomew *(central panel)*; Archangel Gabriel, Saint Petronius, Saint Christopher and Saint Anthony *(left panel)*; Virgin Annunciate, Saint Jerome, a Bishop Saint (Ambrose?) and Saint Florian *(right panel)*

Tempera on panel, central panel 25 x 49.5 cm (9 $^7/_8$ x 19 $^1/_2$ in.), side panels 13 x 49.5 cm (5 $^1/_8$ x 19 $^1/_2$ in.)

Provenance:
Germany, private collection

The present work is a triptych with folding panels intended for personal devotion.

The state of preservation of the support and the painted surface is admirable. The red decoration of the frame has in fact survived intact, and even the gold stars are visible on the Virgin's blue mantle, as are the gold flowers on the red cloth behind her. Similar decorative details have in fact often been lost in other 14th-century panels. It is also possible to admire the raceme decoration executed with the iteration of small points in the halos of the sacred figures, a motif present in other panels by the Bolognese painter Simone di Filippo.[1] The outline of the halos is rendered with a circle of punches, two in the central panel. The painter used a punch with a 'palmetta' inside an oval which Letizia Lodi has recognized only in paintings by Simone di Filippo.[2]

The figurative composition of the triptych, with the *Virgin and Child Enthroned between Saints* in the central panel and the *Annunciation* and *Saints* in the side panels, was common in 14th-century triptychs destined for personal devotion. Various iconographical choices are, however, indicative of Bolognese provenance. Firstly, in the left panel the bust of Saint Petronius holding the city of Bologna indicates this saint as the rebuilder of the city in the Late Antique period. This new iconography became common when the saint was chosen as the first patron of the city during the government of the people and guilds, sanctioned by the statutes of 1376.[3] In the little view of Bologna the Torre degli Asinelli is represented with the 'corridore', the fortification that collapsed during a fire between 1398 and 1399.[4] Secondly, in the right-hand panel is Saint Florian, recognizable by his aristocratic garments, by the sword of a noble knight and by the flower he holds in his hand.[5] Saint Florian also began to be regularly mentioned among the patrons of Bologna from 1376. His cult was linked to that of Petronius, since hagiographic tradition narrates that the relics of Florian were brought to Bologna from the Holy Land by Bishop Petronius himself.[6] The presence of the two co-patrons may suggest that the bishop represented next to Saint Florian is Saint Ambrose, he too being one of the patron saints of Bologna.[7]

As Daniele Benati has rightly asserted, the painting is a valuable work by the Bolognese painter Simone di Filippo, who from the 17th century was known as Simone 'dei Crocifissi'. It is an important addition to the numerous group of triptychs with folding wings that survive from the production of Simone. The relatively large number that have survived to this day is indicative of the painter's prolific output in this genre of objects. The fact that all these triptychs – apart from the splendid Salavin altarpiece housed in the Louvre[8] – show the large bulky forms and simple and direct expressiveness, rendered by means of an accentuated chiaroscuro, of the panels subsequent to the *Madonna di Giovanni da Piacenza* of 1378,

1., 2., 3. Simone di Filippo, called 'dei Crocifissi'
Predella
Bologna, Pinacoteca Nazionale

housed in the Pinacoteca in Bologna,[9] and the *Coronation* of the Opera Pia Zoni of Bologna, dated 1382,[10] may be explained by the particular popularity of Simone's style with private Bolognese patrons in the last decades of the century.

The triptych discussed here can therefore be chronologically placed close to the predella of the Pinacoteca di Bologna (Figg. 1, 2, 3), formerly part of the lost polyptych for the chapel whose patronage the Cospi family acquired in San Petronio in 1396.[11] The painting is also chronologically near the triptych of the Galleria Nazionale di Parma (Fig. 4).[12] Thanks to its better state of preservation, the triptych presented here shows that Simone was able to achieve results of agreeable expressiveness even late in his life, a capacity that evidently earned him an important commission in the prestigious new worksite of the basilica of San Petronio.

Gianluca Del Monaco

4. Simone di Filippo, called 'dei Crocifissi'
Triptych
Parma, Galleria Nazionale

1) L. Lodi, *Note sulla decorazione punzonata di dipinti su tavola di area emiliana dalla metà alla fine del Trecento*, 'Musei Ferraresi. Bollettino annuale', XI, 1981, pp. 93-94 no. 42, 99 no. 46, 101 no. 48.

2) *Ibidem*, p. 203.

3) L. Paolini, *Un patrono condiviso. La figura di san Petronio: da "padre e pastore" a simbolo principale della religione civica bolognese (XII-XIV sec.)*, in *Petronio e Bologna. Il volto di una storia. Arte storia e culto del Santo Patrono*, exh. cat. (Bologna), Ferrara 2001, pp. 77-83.

4) S. Battistini, in *Petronio e Bologna* cit., p. 254, no. 4.

5) G. Kaftal, *Iconography of the Saints in the Painting of North East Italy*, Florence 1978, coll. 321-322, no. 105.

6) R. Pini, *Ascesa, trionfo e oblio di un patrono cittadino. San Flo-*riano di Bologna nella storia e nell'iconografia, 'Atti e memorie della R. Deputazione di Storia Patria per le Province di Romagna', LVIII, 2007, pp. 222, 224.

7) L. Paolini, *Un patrono condiviso* cit., p. 82.

8) M. Ferretti, *Simone dei Crocifissi*, in F. Arcangeli, *Pittura bolognese del '300*, Bologna 1978, pp. 188-189, fig. 79, pl. XL.

9) F. Lollini, in *Pinacoteca Nazionale di Bologna. Catalogo generale*, I, *Dal Duecento a Francesco Francia*, Venice 2004, pp. 144-146, no. 40.

10) O. Bergomi, *La chiesa di Santa Maria Incoronata*, in *Bologna*, 'Il carrobbio', XXIX, 2003, pp. 86-87.

11) F. Lollini, in *Pinacoteca Nazionale* cit., pp. 150-152, no. 43.

12) L. Fornari Schianchi, *La Galleria Nazionale di Parma*, Parma 1983, pp. 32-33.

SIMONE DI FILIPPO, CALLED 'DEI CROCIFISSI'

Bologna, documented from 1354, died 1399

6. Christ on the Cross with the Mourning Virgin, Saint John the Evangelist and Saint Mary Magdalen

Tempera on panel, 33 x 43 cm (13 x 17 in.)

Provenance:
Private collection

This trapezoidal panel may originally have formed the central pinnacle of a polyptych or the central panel of a triptych with folding panels or even one of the two parts of a diptych made for personal devotion. The absence of the original cornice prevents us from advancing more precise hypotheses on the type of object under examination.

The painting is on the whole in a good state of preservation, although the gilding of the background appears impoverished, in some areas revealing the red-coloured base preparation, and the figures have lost some of the finishings that must have softened the chiaroscuro contrasts. Still fully visible is the punched decoration on the halos of the four protagonists. The punch used consisted of a 'palmetta' within an oval, corresponding to type 43 of the classification carried out years ago by Letizia Lodi, who identified this type of punch only in the paintings of Simone di Filippo.[1]

The iconography of the *Crucified Christ on the Cross with Mourners* is a simplified version of the *Crucifixion*, a scene particularly appropriate for meditation in front of the image.[2] The choice of this subject in the painting on wood of the Italian Trecento was normally combined with the *Coronation of the Virgin*, an image that emphasized the role of Mary, mother of Christ and queen of the Church, in the redemption of mankind, made possible through the sacrifice of her Son on the Cross.

The painting appears in this context for the first time. The attribution to the Bolognese painter Simone di Filippo, called 'dei Crocifissi' at the time of the Counter-reformation, was proposed by Daniele Benati and is confirmed by a comparison with other works by the painter representing the same subject, including notably the central pinnacle of the signed polyptych no. 298 of the Pinacoteca Nazionale di Bologna (Fig. 1).[3] In these works, which in all probability are chronologically near the predella of the polyptych executed not before 1396 for the Cospi chapel in San Petronio, today in the Pinacoteca Nazionale di Bologna (nos. 274-275),[4] Simone shows that he has now acquired a consistent formal style in which he consolidates the lively expressiveness of the early decades of activity, observable for example in the *Crucifixions* of polyptych no. 254 of the Pinacoteca di Bologna[5] or the panel of the Detroit Institute of Arts.[6] The somewhat bulky figures are arranged within a simplified setting and their faces, made grim by the accentuated chiaroscuro and by their simplified features, contribute to communicating the *pathos* of the scene in a direct and immediately comprehensible way.

The success obtained with his Bolognese patrons and the easy replicability of Simone's mature style may explain the oscillating quality of the painter's works, noted for the first time by Roberto Longhi.[7] In fact, the increase in the artist's production, confirmed by the

1. Simone di Filippo, called 'dei Crocifissi'
Crucifixion
Bologna, Pinacoteca Nazionale

2. Simone di Filippo, called 'dei Crocifissi'
Crucified Christ among Mourners
Florence, Ergas collection (formerly)

fairly large number of surviving paintings to be placed chronologically between the *Madonna di Giovanni da Piacenza* of 1378[8] and the predella of the Cospi polyptych of ca. 1396, inevitably meant that the quality varied considerably according to the amount of work put into it, in general consistently high in the paintings destined for ecclesiastical use. Although not reaching the level of the central pinnacle of polyptych no. 298 of the Pinacoteca di Bologna, the panel under examination is nonetheless of an average and appreciable quality, being perhaps comparable with the *Crucified Christ among Mourners* formerly in the Ergas collection in Florence (Fig. 2),[9] of a similar format, in the same scene represented in the central compartment of the triptych with folding panels of the Ashmolean Museum of Oxford (Fig. 3)[10] and in the signed *Coronation* of the Pinacoteca Civica di Pavia (Fig. 4).[11]

Gianluca Del Monaco

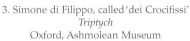

3. Simone di Filippo, called 'dei Crocifissi'
Triptych
Oxford, Ashmolean Museum

4. Simone di Filippo, called 'dei Crocifissi'
Coronation
Pavia, Pinacoteca Civica

1) L. Lodi, *Note sulla decorazione punzonata di dipinti su tavola di area emiliana dalla metà alla fine del Trecento*, 'Musei Ferraresi. Bollettino annuale', XI, 1981, p. 203.

2) H. Belting, *L'arte e il suo pubblico. Funzione e forme delle antiche immagini della passione*, Bologna 1986, pp. 47-58.

3) F. Lollini, in *Pinacoteca Nazionale di Bologna. Catalogo generale*, I, *Dal Duecento a Francesco Francia*, Venice 2004, p. 146, no. 41.

4) *Ibidem*, pp. 150-152, no. 43.

5) *Ibidem*, pp. 132-134, no. 34.

6) M. Ferretti, *Simone dei Crocifissi*, in F. Arcangeli, *Pittura bolognese del '300*, Bologna 1978, p. 196.

7) R. Longhi, *La pittura dell'Italia del Trecento nell'Italia settentrionale (1934-1935)*, in *Edizione delle opere complete di R. L.*, VI, *Lavori in Valpadana*, Florence 1973, p. 62.

8) F. Lollini, in *Pinacoteca Nazionale* cit., pp. 144-146, no. 40.

9) Z. Bonacini, *Alcuni dipinti primitivi della scuola emiliana in collezioni private*, 'Cronache d'arte', IV, 1927, p. 322, fig. 3.

10) C. Lloyd, *A catalogue of the earlier Italian paintings in the Ashmolean Museum*, Oxford 1977, pp. 162-163, fig. 118.

11) G. Giacomelli Vedovello, in *Pavia. Pinacoteca Malaspina*, Pavia 1981, p. 216.

Gherardo di Jacopo Starnina

Florence, documented 1387-1409, deceased before 1413

7. Virgin and Child with Saint Nicholas of Bari and Saint Stephen

Tempera on panel, 96 x 50.5 cm (37 ³/₄ x 19 ⁷/₈ in.)

Provenance:
Richmond (Sussex), Sir Francis Ferdinand Maurice Cook
London, M. H. Drey collection (sale at Sotheby's, London, 12 May 1955)
Lucerne, E. and M. Kofler-Truniger collection
Paris, private collection

Freed from its former inner frame in the shape of a trilobe – a later addition of the 19th century which was duly removed during the last careful restoration – this exceptionally well-preserved painting is now revealed all its stunning beauty.

The present painting, commissioned, as we shall see, as an object of private devotion, has retained its original golden gilt frame and follows a well-established canon for such objects which, because of their high ornate gable, at the time of their production were called "colmi".[1] These were shaped like a tabernacle with – in the case of the present painting – twisted wooden columns painted in gold surmounted by a high and lavishly embellished gable. This ornate wooden architecture splendidly frames a graciously painted heavenly vision. The Virgin and her Child appear slightly elevated on a cloud and are adored by two flanking saints, Saint Nicholas of Bari on the left and Saint Stephen on the right, who, with seemingly incredulous eyes, witness this privileged vision of heavenly bliss. The crescent moon below the Virgin's feet alludes to the Woman of the Apocalypse. In fact, during the 12th and 13th century, Saint Bernard and Saint Bonaventure understood the "Woman clothed with the sun" in Saint John's Book of Revelations (12:1 ff.) as the Virgin, at the same time presenting an interpretation that celebrates her motherhood which was ultimately at the basis of the faithful's hope in her intercession for mankind – hence the victory over evil. Such thoughts were the very essence of the faithful's contemplation during his private prayer in front of such a painting. It is no surprise, therefore, to find on the base of the painting a written reference to the Virgin's motherhood, the angel's words addressed to her during his revelation of her future motherhood: "AVE MARIA GRACIA PLENA". The same words were also those addressed to her by the faithful during their prayers in front of this picture, and therefore by the members of the Lorini and Venturi families who, as is confirmed by the coats-of-arms on the base of the painting, had commissioned it.

Since the painting's first documentation in the short-list of works of the E. and M. Kofler-Truniger collection, presented in 1964 in the Kunsthaus of Zurich, our picture had always been associated with the painterly world of Gherardo di Jacopo Starnina. In the above-mentioned inventory, which in the case of our picture offered no further art-historical comment, the *Madonna* was merely listed as a work by the then still anonymous painter known as the "Master of the Bambino Vispo", an appellation coined by Osvald Sirén in 1904 by reason of the artist's allegedly vivacious characterization of the Christ Child.[2] This association with the bulk of works grouped around Sirén's "Master of the Bambino Vispo" was never challenged by later scholars and was resumed by Boskovits and Fremantle in 1975.

Since Sirén's study on the "Master of the Bambino Vispo" scholars rightfully recognized a distinct Spanish touch in the art of this then still mysterious painter and thought of associating his oeuvre with the Florentine painter Gherardo di Jacopo Starnina, who was highly praised by Vasari[3] and known to have worked in the last decade of the 14th century in Valencia.[4] The identification of the so-called "Master of the Bambino Vispo" with Starnina, however, seemed out of the question, as long as one was convinced that a partially reconstructed altarpiece, the so-called Saint Lawrence altarpiece (Fig. 1),[5] should be identified as the one commissioned in 1422 by Cardinal Pietro Corsini (who was thought to figure in the painting together with Saint Lawrence) for a chapel in the cathedral of Florence. As a matter of fact, the date 1422 for the commissioning of this altarpiece, allegedly identifiable with the one dedicated to Saint Lawrence, appeared to be at odds with Starnina's biography owing to the year of his death (before 1413).

The obstacle for an identification of Starnina was removed only when Cornelia Syre and Jeanne van Waadenoijen independently discovered that the cardinal in Carthusian dress, presented by Saint Lawrence on the panel in the Staatliche Gemäldegalerie in Berlin, was not Pietro Corsini, but the famous cardinal Angelo Acciaiuoli, who had been buried in the

1. Gherardo di Jacopo Starnina
Reconstruction of the Saint Lawrence altarpiece

2. Lorenzo Monaco
Angel of the Annunciation
Private collection

Certosa di Galluzzo near Florence in 1408, shortly after he had commissioned for this church an altarpiece, i.e. the one in question dedicated to Saint Lawrence.[6]

This new situation in the scholarly assessment of the "Master of the Bambino Vispo" and his now ascertained identity with the documented Gherardo di Jacopo Starnina not only finally confirmed a long-standing scholarly intuition but also paved the way for a firm chronological indication for his oeuvre. As a matter of fact most of his work, with the exception of the paintings relating to his activity in Spain, which date from the last decade of the 14th century, was painted in a relatively short period of ten years (ca. 1403-1413). Starnina's return to Florence in the very early years of the 15th century, which introduced there a first-hand knowledge of the Gothic world of Spain, had quite noticeable repercussions in the production of art in and around Florence. It encouraged there the breakthrough of an international Gothic of vibrant elegance based on courtly aesthetic ideals, an innovation enthusiastically welcomed by artists like Lorenzo Monaco, to name but the most important of the Florentine painters who at the beginning of the Quattrocento attempted a translation of these influences into a local Florentine Gothic style.

To appreciate the immediate influence of Starnina on Lorenzo Monaco's work and their general artistic interdependance it is enough to compare the recently rediscovered fragment of an angel of the Annunciation by Lorenzo Monaco in a private collection, datable to the years around 1408 (Fig. 2), with the profile of some angels from Starnina's Acciaiuoli altarpiece, those in a private collection and the music-making angel on the left of the panel in the Boijmans van Beuningen Museum in Rotterdam (Fig. 3). Nowhere in his paintings produced in Tuscany are Starnina's experiences with Spanish art so evident as in this angel, in whose animated blond curls – in contrast to Lorenzo Monaco's generally simpler, though no less effective stylizations – we notice more accentuated and at the same time livelier zig-zag undulations that undoubtedly recall the abstractive formulas of Spanish late Trecento painting, which had developed as a result of the growing receptivity of Spanish painters toward transalpine art.

3. Gherardo di Jacopo Starnina
Angel (detail)
Rotterdam, Boijmans van Beuningen Museum

Notwithstanding Starnina's relatively short activity in Florence during a time span of just over a decade, his impact on Florentine painters was considerable. It reached not only, as we have seen, the most refined Florentine painter, Lorenzo Monaco, but was felt also by other artists in and around Florence and others still from neighbouring towns such as Lucca. A painting like Masolino's magnificent *Madonna of Humility* in the Uffizi Gallery in Florence is hardly imaginable without taking account of the artist's deeper interest in Starnina's art, a fact that would seem to lend a certain credibility to Vasari's assertion that Masolino had trained in Starnina's atelier. No less evident is Starnina's influence on painters of a minor calibre, such as Rossello di Jacopo Franchi or the somewhat rustic Scolaio di Giovanni (ex-Master of Borgo a Collina).

The chronological assessment of our splendid *Madonna* within Starnina's oeuvre emerges from stylistic observations which clearly establish an artistic relation with the crucial Acciaiuoli altarpiece (painted shortly before 1407), which, as we will see shortly, is confirmed by the historical context of the painting. As far as style is concerned, the artistic relationship between the *Virgin Annunciate* of this altarpiece (Frankfurt, Städel Museum; Fig. 4) and our *Madonna*, who appears as a sister to her, is quite remarkable. No less evident is the relation between our painting and other paintings by Starnina, such as the highly vibrant and elegant depiction of the *Virgin and Child Enthroned* surrounded by an animated host of adoring and music-making angels in the John Paul Getty Museum in Los Angeles (Fig. 5), or the *Virgin and Child with Saint John the Baptist, Saint Nicholas of Bari and four Angels* in the Galleria dell'Accademia in Florence (Fig. 6). The sinuous, slightly elongated and therefore seemingly weightless figures of our painting lead directly to the spirit of the Getty panel which, despite its crowdedness, appears as a weightless and well-measured symphony of lines and motion. Despite the fact that there are only a few figures in our picture it has lost none of

its compact, well-balanced character, and in this, as well as in the subtle linear cadences, it shares all the highly sophisticated rhythmic qualities of the Getty Museum *Madonna*.

The stylistic observations which, as we have seen, place our picture in the chronological vicinity of the Acciaiuoli altarpiece, ca. 1407, find an interesting confirmation in the historical circumstances surrounding it. The lead to the picture's history comes from the already mentioned coat-of-arms painted on the carpentry in the lower section of the painting. Painted on the base of the lateral columns, they refer, on the left, to the Lorini family and, on the right, to the Venturi family, both members of the Florentine merchant élite. This suggests that Starnina's painting was probably executed on the occasion of the wedding of Antonio di Filippo Lorini and Agnola di Jacopo di Francesco Venturi which took place in the year 1407.

This wedding was possibly the fruit of an economic alliance between these successful and important Florentine families of merchants. Antonio di Filippo Lorini, who seems to have

4. Gherardo di Jacopo Starnina
Virgin Annunciate
Frankfurt, Städel Museum

5. Gherardo di Jacopo Starnina
Virgin and Child Enthroned
Los Angeles, John Paul Getty Museum

6. Gherardo di Jacopo Starnina
Virgin and Child with Saints
Florence, Galleria dell'Accademia

commissioned the painting for his wedding with the daughter of the influential Jacopo di Francesco Venturi, member of the Signoria from 1396 and member of the 'Arte del Cambio', the Moneychangers' Guild,[7] was himself a rich and successful Florentine merchant. He probably followed in the footsteps of his father Filippo Lorini, who as a merchant in the wool trade was a member of the influential 'Arte di Calimala' in Florence, the rich corporation of cloth merchants and the most influential and most prestigious guild in the city. Venturi was a partner in Venice of the powerful Florentine banker Vieri di Cambio de' Medici,[8] while Antonio di Filippo Lorini was active in the entourage of Francesco Datini and is documented in the 1390s as having been involved in affairs between Tuscany and Spain, particularly in Majorca and Barcelona.[9] As a matter of fact, between 1382-1401 he is documented as having managed a business branch of his own in Florence and another in Barcelona together with a partner, a certain Michele di Simone.[10]

From these biographical dates we might gain some ideas on two key issues regarding this painting; first its iconography, which shows the Virgin and Child adored by Saint Stephen and Saint Nicholas of Bari, and second, the decision of Gherardo di Jacopo Starnina to carry out this particular artistic commission.

The fact that the patron Antonio di Filippo Lorini engaged in trade between Tuscany, Catalonia and Majorca, where, as we have already mentioned, he ran a Barcelona-based business between 1382 and 1401 – therefore essentially at the same time as Starnina's activity in Spain – might provide a clue as to why his choice for the picture fell on Starnina. It may have been the fruit of a long-lasting acquaintance within the Florentine community in Catalonia. Following his return to Florence in 1401, on the occasion of his wedding with Agnola di Jacopo di Francesco Venturi in 1407, Lorini may have remembered his now internationally celebrated fellow citizen Starnina, who had also returned to Florence around 1403 to make himself available for artistic commissions. Lorini might therefore have preferred Starnina to well-established Florentine painters and ordered from him the painting which was to serve for private devotion in the home of the newly-wedded couple.

The pictorial programme of this precious painting comes straight to the point, insofar as the choice of saints reflects the patron's own biography. As the patron saint of the Arte di Calimala, Lorini's own guild, Saint Stephen was the most appropriate choice for the painting. The same was true of Saint Nicholas on the opposite side, in that being the patron saint of merchants and moneylenders he was the figure most suited to represent the banking activities of the young bride's family, the Venturi.

Starnina's breathtakingly elegant *Madonna* turned out to be a splendid household object belonging to a sophisticated member of the wealthy Florentine bourgeoisie. The historical circumstances of the executing painter and his patron – both members of the community of Florentine professionals active in Spain in the 1390s – offer an interesting insight into the workings of professional relations between artists and patrons.

With his luminous palette, and the measured elegance and expressiveness of his figures, Starnina created a work of the highest grace. These were qualities that immediately impressed his Florentine contemporaries and had a lasting effect on Florentine art that would persist well after Masaccio's, Masolino's and Fra Angelico's revolutionary artistic experiments which unmistakeably heralded the new artistic vision of the Florentine Renaissance.

Gaudenz Freuler

1) Cf. *Neri di Bicci Ricordanze (10 marzo 1453-24 aprile 1475)*, ed. B. Santi, Pisa 1976, *passim*.

2) O. Sirén, *Di alcuni pittori fiorentini che subirono l'influenza di Lorenzo Monaco. Il Maestro del Bambino Vispo*, 'L'Arte', VII, 1904, pp. 337-355.

3) G. Vasari, *Le Vite de' più eccellenti Pittori scultori ed Architettori*, II (ed. Milanesi), Florence 1878, pp. 5-10.

4) For a more recent assessment of Starnina's career cf. A. De Marchi, in *Sumptuosa Tabula picta. Pittori a Lucca tra gotico e rinascimento*, exh. cat. (Lucca, Museo Villa Guinigi, 28.3.-5.7.1998), Livorno 1998, p. 260 ff., and R. Hiller von Gaertringen, *Italienische Gemälde im Städel 1300-1550*, Mainz am Rhein 2004, pp. 186-202.

5) For a recent discussion of this altarpiece cf. R. Hiller von

Gaertringen, *Italienische Gemälde* cit.

6) C. Syre, *Studien zum "Maestro del Bambino Vispo" und Starnina*, Bonn 1979, pp. 8 ff., 17 ff.; J. van Waadenoijen, *Starnina e il gotico internazionale a Firenze*, Florence 1982, p. 54 ff.; R. Hiller von Gaertringen, *Italienische Gemälde* cit.

7) J. F. Padgett, P. D. Mc Lean, *Organizational Invention and Elite Transformation: The Birth of Partnership Systems in Renaissance Florence*, 'American Journal of Sociology', 111, 5, 2006, pp. 1477-1478.

8) *Ibidem*, pp. 1549-1550.

9) G. Nigro, *Mercanti in Maiorca. Il carteggio datiniano dall'isola (1387-1396)*, Florence 2003, *passim*.

10) J. F. Padgett, P. D. Mc Lean, *Organizational Invention* cit., pp. 1558-1559.

Bibliography:

Die Sammlung E. M. Kofler-Truniger, exh. cat. (Zurich, Kunsthaus), Zürich 1964, no. 951

M. Boskovits, *Il maestro del Bambino Vispo: Gherardo Starnina o Miguel Alcaniz?*, 'Paragone', 307, 1975, pp. 14-15, n. 1, fig. 9

R. Fremantle, *Florentine Gothic Painters*, London 1975, p. 443

C. Syre, *Studien zum "Maestro del Bambino Vispo" und Starnina*, Bonn 1979, pp. 97-100, 103 and 109

J. van Waadenoijen, *Starnina e il gotico internazionale a Firenze*, Florence 1982, pp. 69, 82, fig. 57

G. Freuler, *Künder der wunderbaren Dinge, frühe italienische Malerei aus Sammlungen in der Schweiz und in Liechtenstein*, Thyssen-Bornemisza, Lugano-Castagnola, April-June 1991, p. 222, fig. 86.

JACOPO DI CIONE

Florence, documented 1365-1400

8. Virgin and Child with Angels

Tempera on panel, 81.5 x 50.3 cm (32 x 19 ⁴/₅ in.)

Inscriptions: on the scroll:"EGO SUM VIA VERITAS ET VITA"; at the base:"AVE. DULCIS. VIRGO MARIA. SUCCURRE NOBIS MATER PIA ANNI DOMINI MCCCLXXXVI"

Provenance:
Florence, Count Felice Miari Pelli Fabbroni collection
Florence, Carlo De Carlo collection
Florence, Lisa De Carlo collection

The work has survived in an extremely satisfactory condition, inside its original frame, though without the small twisted columns at the sides.

The painting represents the iconographical theme of the Madonna of Humility, one of the most common representations in Italian painting from the middle of the 14th century, in the most sumptuous and pre-courtly variations, with the Virgin lying on the ground on a precious brocade supported by two angels. The Child, sitting on the Virgin's knee, is in a hieratically frontal position and in the act of blessing with his right hand raised, while in his left hand is a scroll bearing the inscription:"EGO SUM VIA VERITAS ET VITA". Around Jesus's neck is a bright red branch of coral which alludes to his future sacrifice on the Cross. In the base is the following invocation to the Madonna:"AVE. DULCIS. VIRGO MARIA. SUCCURRE NOBIS MATER PIA ANNI DOMINI MCCCLXXXVI". An identical invocation reappears in at least two other Florentine paintings of the period attributed to Giovanni del Biondo:[1] these are the *Virgin and Child* and above the *Crucifixion* of the Pinacoteca Nazionale di Siena (inv. no. 584), signed and dated 1377[2] and the other *Virgin and Child* with members of the Compagni family (Fig. 1) from the church of San Felice a Ema (Florence) bearing the date 1387.[3]

The work is mentioned for the first time in the *Corpus of Florentine Painting*[4] as being owned by Count Felice Miari Pelli Fabbroni of Florence and with an attribution to the so-called "Master of the Annunciation of Prato", in his view a late follower of Orcagna,[5] the author, that is, of a wood panel with the Annunciation and, in the predella, the Stories of Christ in the church of the Holy Spirit in Prato (Fig. 4). Boskovits[6] later convincingly attributed to the artistic production of Jacopo di Cione those paintings attributed by Offner to various anonymous painters who he imagined gravitated around the workshop of the Orcagna brothers, including also the supposed "Master of the Annunciation of Prato", in particular on the basis of an analysis of the present painting. Boskovits also drew attention to its evident stylistic similarity to the *Virgin and Child* (Fig. 2) of the church of Sant'Agata at Scarperia, this painting also attributed by him to Jacopo di Cione and which, on the basis of documentary evidence discovered in more recent years,[7] originally bore – when in the middle of a triptych that was later dismembered – an inscription with the date 1383. Our painting is also reproduced as a work by Jacopo di Cione in Richard Fremantle's invaluable compendium on Florentine painters.[8] The reconstruction of the late activity of the youngest of the Orcagna brothers and, in particular, the attribution to him of the ex-Miari Pelli Fabbroni *Virgin* has been generally accepted by later critics.[9]

Aue dulcis uirgo maria · Succhurre no
bis mater pia · Anni domini mccclxxxvi

1. Giovanni del Biondo
Virgin and Child with members of the Compagni family
San Felice a Ema (Florence), church of San Felice

2. Jacopo di Cione
Virgin and Child
Scarperia (Florence), church of Sant'Agata

As far as I am concerned, I have already had occasion to mention the more recent belonging of the painting to De Carlo, underlining its importance in the career of Jacopo di Cione, in the 'entry' for the *Dizionario biografico degli italiani*,[10] as well as the influence of the contemporary activity of Giovanni del Biondo noticeable in it, as already pointed out by Boskovits. Undoubtedly, the adoption, common to both artists, of the inscription with the supplication to the Madonna reported here represents an important connection between the two workshops. These established Florentine painters also found themselves collaborating on a single work, in a way that is in a certain sense inexplicable to us, documenting the exercise of *connoisseurship* at the highest level: in the altarpiece painted by Giovanni del Biondo for the cathedral of Florence with *Saint Zenobius Enthroned between two Allegorical Figures and Saints Eugene and Crescentius*, Jacopo di Cione executed the figure of Saint Eugene (Fig. 3) kneeling down at bottom left.[11] At the same time the two artists maintained their own individual and highly characteristic styles. Giovanni del Biondo never arrived at the almost maniacal penchant for preciousness that emerges from the decoration of the fabrics – with recourse to a refined interpretation of the 'sgraffito' technique – demonstrated also in the present work by Jacopo di Cione. It was, however, precisely this exquisite technical and

3. Jacopo di Cione
Saint Eugene (detail)
Florence, cathedral

4. Jacopo di Cione
Annunciation
Prato, church of the Holy Spirit

decorative perfectionism and the ability to render the corporeal masses of his figures concretely plausible, that represented the hallmark of his late artistic activity, as is revealed at the highest level by the impeccable *Virgin* belonging to Carlo De Carlo.

The artist would later propose what might be described in a finally appropriate way as 'accademia orcagnesca' up to the last decade of the century, in the noble and still powerful triptych of the Academy of Arts of Honolulu bearing the date 1391. A work of lofty workmanship and dignity which nonetheless proved dramatically out of fashion on the Florentine artistic scene, dominated as it was at this time by Agnolo Gaddi and Spinello Aretino, painters who showed a seemingly inexhaustible creative vein and were open, each in a different and original way, to the innovations of the late Gothic period.

Angelo Tartuferi

1) R. Offner, K. Steinweg, *A Critical and Historical Corpus of Florentine Painting*, Sec. IV, V, *Giovanni del Biondo* (part. II), New York 1969, p. 36, no. 1; M. Boskovits, *Pittura fiorentina alla vigilia del Rinascimento*, Florence 1975, p. 325.
2) P. Torriti, *La Pinacoteca Nazionale di Siena. I dipinti dal XII al XV secolo*, Genoa 1980, pp. 230-231.
3) M. Boskovits, p. 310.
4) R. Offner, K. Steinweg, *A Critical and Historical Corpus* cit., p. 36, no. 1.
5) M. Boskovits, *Pittura fiorentina* cit., pp. 226-227, note 68; R. Offner, *A Critical and Historical Corpus of Florentine Painting*, Supplement by H. B. J. Maginnis, *A Legacy of Attributions*, Glückstadt 1981.

6) M. Boskovits, *Pittura fiorentina* cit., pp. 94-95 and 325.
7) L. Brunori Cianti, *Il patrimonio artistico*, in Various Authors, *Scarperia. Storia, Arte, Artigianato*, Firenze 1990, p. 47.
8) R. Fremantle, *Florentine Gothic painters: from Giotto to Masaccio; a guide to painting in and near Florence, 1300 to 1450*, London 1975, p. 170 and fig. 336.
9) E. S. Skaug, *Punch marks from Giotto to Beato Angelico*, Oslo 1994, vol. I, p. 195.
10) A. Tartuferi, *Iacopo di Cione*, in *Dizionario biografico degli italiani*, 52, Rome 2004, pp. 58-59.
11) M. Boskovits, *Pittura fiorentina* cit., pp. 95, 226 note 65 and 307.

Bibliography:

R. Offner, K.Steinweg, *A critical and historical corpus of Florentine painting*, Sec. IV, Vol. V (Part II), *Giovanni del Biondo*, New York 1969, p. 36, no. 1

R. Fremantle, *Florentine Gothic painters: from Giotto to Masaccio; a guide to painting in and near Florence, 1300 to 1450*, London 1975, p. 170, and fig. 336

M. Boskovits, *Pittura fiorentina alla vigilia del Rinascimento*, Florence 1975, p. 325, fig. 120

A. Tartuferi, in *Le opere del ricordo. Opere d'arte dal XIV al XVI secolo appartenute a Carlo De Carlo, presentate dalla figlia Lisa*, ed. A. Tartuferi, Florence 2007, pp. 24-27, cat. 3 (from which this entry has been taken).

MASTER OF THE RICHARDSON TRIPTYCH

Siena, ca. 1370-1415

9. Virgin and Child Enthroned with Angels and Saints; the Redeemer; the Annunciation

Tempera on panel, open 77.5 x 57.4 cm (30 $^1/_2$ x 22 $^3/_5$ in.)

Provenance:
Florence, Charles Loeser collection, 1918
London, Matthiesen Gallery, 1983
Florence, Carlo De Carlo collection
Florence, Lisa De Carlo collection

This delightful triptych is remarkably well preserved; the altarpiece has retained its side panels and the chalk paste decoration ornamenting the three compartments is almost intact. The well-preserved pictorial surface shows small losses the paint here and there, a phenomenon more noticeable along the lower edge of the central panel. There are occasional scratches, and some abrasions can be seen in the gold leaf, especially in the left wing. A comparison with the photograph of the painting published by Berenson in 1918,[1] when the triptych was in the Loeser collection in Florence, shows no significant change in its condition.

The triptych rests on a wooden base, originally decorated with silver: darkened traces of the silver leaf remain over the base preparation. The use of silver in place of the gold leaf that is used on other parts of the woodwork raises doubts about whether the base originally belonged to the triptych. In it, decorated along the edges with carved and punched bands, we observe on the other hand the use of the same punch in the form of a five-petalled rosette which also embellishes the gold frames of the triptych, an element that would seem therefore to corroborate the original unity of the whole. Carved in the centre of the front side of the base is a medallion bearing a coat-of-arms in the form of a shield with three horizontal bands, today devoid of their colour. The back of the work is painted with an application of white colour, this being original, while the blue colour covering the verso of the two leafs has probably been repainted.

The triptych represents the Virgin and Child, the former sitting on a high-backed throne entirely covered in a cloth; the decorative motif of the fabric, carved into the gold leaf, was widely used in Sienese circles in the second half of the 14th century.[2]

The Child in the act of blessing holds a scroll with the inscription "FIAT", which comes from a passage in the Bible ("dixitque Deus fiat lux et facta est lux", Genesis 1:4). Behind the throne are six praying angels, while in the right-hand panel is a representation of Saint Catherine of Alexandria, recognizable by the presence of the spiked wheel and the book she is holding; the palm leaf symbolizing the saint's martyrdom possibly the result of a repainting, appears to be incongruous given the pose of the hand. On the other side, to the right of the Virgin, another saint of noble descent holds a book and a slender cross; such attributes might suggest a Saint Helen, although possible identifications with other saints, such as Saint Agatha or Saint Juliana, cannot be excluded.[3]

In the left panel, Saint John the Baptist is holding a scroll on which a passage from the Gospels is written: "ECCE AGNUS DEI ECCE" ("qui tollit peccata mundi", John 1:29), while

1. Master of the Richardson Triptych
Virgin and Child with Saints
Siena, Pinacoteca Nazionale

beside him is the apostle Andrew holding the cross of martyrdom and a fish, alluding to the fact that he was a fisherman.[4] Represented in the other panel are James the Apostle, with his pilgrim's bag and staff, and Saint Anthony Abbot, carrying a cross in the shape of a T, the "sertum precatorium" and a small bell. The representation is completed by three tondos containing the figures of the Archangel Gabriel, the Virgin Annunciate and in the centre Christ Blessing.

The work was in the Loeser collection in Florence in 1918; later on the antique market, it appeared at the Matthiesen Gallery in London in 1983 and later entered the collection of Carlo De Carlo; it was presented at the Semenzato auction in Florence in 2003.

The painting was published by Berenson in 1918 with an attribution to Cola Petruccioli; the scholar placed the tabernacle in the area of late 14th-century Sienese painting, describing the artist as "a double of Fei". The attribution to Cola Petruccioli, however, accepted by De

2. Master of the Richardson Triptych
Virgin and Child with Saints
New York, Metropolitan Museum of Art (formerly)

Nicola and Gnoli,[5] was not reproposed by Berenson in the Indexes of 1932, where the work is not mentioned. In the meantime the attribution to Cola had been refuted by van Marle.[6] Considered by Kaftal to belong to the circle of Paolo di Giovanni Fei, the triptych was included by Federico Zeri[7] within a group of works which included the panel representing Mary (no. 142) from the Pinacoteca Nazionale di Siena (Fig. 1) and the triptych with the *Virgin and Saints* (1888.3.2.) formerly at the Metropolitan Museum of New York (now in a private collection, Fig. 2).[8] The group is catalogued in the Fototeca of the Fondazione Federico Zeri under the conventional name of the Master of the Antinori Triptych, deriving from a painting in the Antinori collection at Celsa di Sovicille.[9] The stylistic enucleation of this anonymous painter, who emerged from the circle of Paolo di Giovanni Fei, partly coincides with the independent reconstruction worked by Everett Fahy, who instead baptized the group with the conventional name of "Master of the Richardson Triptych" which derives

3. Master of the Richardson Triptych
Virgin and Child with Saints
Milan, Museo Diocesano

from a triptych with the *Virgin and Child with Saints* in the Fogg Art Museum in Cambridge (Mass.) (inv. 1921.2).

The triptych has been attributed to the Master of the Richardson Triptych, a name enjoying a wider diffusion, by Fahy (written communication and 2008, see bibliography), by Miklós Boskovits (oral communication), by Marilena Tamassia,[10] who dates it to the beginning of the 15th century, noticing in it the influence of Taddeo di Bartolo and relating it to the triptych formerly at the Metropolitan Museum of New York, and by Andrea De Marchi,[11] who considers the painting to be an early work by the master.

The altarpiece was instead presented by Carlo Volpe as a late work of Francesco di Vannuccio in the entry of the Matthiesen catalogue;[12] this attribution was reproposed in the Semenzato auction catalogue in 2003.

4. Master of the Richardson Triptych
Virgin and Child with Saints
London, Weingraf Old Master Gallery (formerly)

Although unconvincing, Volpe's attribution draws attention to the neo-Martinian tone of the group of the *Virgin and Child*, which significantly finds numerous emulators among late 14th-century Sienese painters; the polygonal dais at the base of the throne, a re-elaboration of Sienese prototypes in vogue in the first half of the century, is also taken up in works dating from the end of the third quarter of the 14th century, as in triptych no. 183 of the Pinacoteca Nazionale di Siena, a work arguably by Francesco di Vannuccio, or in the small panel representing the Virgin Mary from the Crespi collection, today in the Museo Diocesano di Milano (Fig. 3), considered by Sonia Chiodo to be a Sienese work of the third quarter and by Boskovits near to the Richardson triptych.[13]

The convergence of opinions in favour of the Master of the Richardson Triptych / Master of the Antinori Triptych certainly merits careful reflection, considering that in 1918 Berenson had already noted similarities between the De Carlo triptych and the former 1888.3.2 altarpiece of the Metropolitan Museum of Art in New York. In line with the style of the anonymous master are the rhythmic coils with which the edges of the cloaks are rendered, the faces characterized by short noses and puckered mouths, a facile translation of models deriving particularly from Paolo di Giovanni Fei, to whom is also referrable the elaborate play of folds, albeit resolved in a more mechanical way. Nor does the broad face of the Virgin and the acutely plastic modelling of the faces appear to be free from the influence of the recently constituted Cristoforo di Bindoccio-Meo di Pero group, of whom the Master of the Richardson Triptych seems to have been a parallel also in the decorative taste that prompts him to favour an abundant working of the gold leaf or the placing of the figures on sumptuous marble floors.

Still lacking is an accurate chronological reconstruction of the artistic career of the Master of the Richardson Triptych, whose works composed mainly of paintings destined for private worship provides few cues for historical and documentary investigation.[14] The only chronological foothold is represented by a small Biccherna panel in the Siena State Archive, dated 1385;[15] the date confirms the stylistic reading of the works which seems to place the activity of the painter in the last third of the 14th century, with possible appendages in the very early years of the following century.

As already observed by De Marchi, the De Carlo triptych seems to be one of the earliest pieces of the catalogue, comparable in its compositional and decorative structure with works of the eighth decade by Niccolò di Buonaccorso, Paolo di Giovanni Fei, Francesco di Vannuccio. The work reveals the inspired descriptive style of the master, who was able to dwell with meticulous attention on the attributes of the saints and on the elegant inscriptions of the scrolls, revealing remarkable skill in the execution, and proving that he was capable of competing with the contemporary workshops of such established artists as the Master of Panzano, or Cristoforo di Bindoccio-Meo di Pero. Among the works ascribed to the anonymous master, there are convincing affinities with the *Madonna* of the Museo Diocesano di Milano (Fig. 3), although the comparison cannot be taken too far given the mediocre condition of the Milanese painting, with the Cambridge triptych, and with the panel representing the Virgin attributed to him by Zeri at the Weingraf Old Master Gallery in London (Fig. 4; Fototeca Fondazione Federico Zeri, PI_0079, ins. 6, entry 7777), where the figure of James the Apostle is very similar. The well-constructed modelling of the faces, which in the best cases seems to emulate Paolo di Giovanni Fei, and the sentimental intonation of the De Carlo triptych seem to be less present in later works, like the painting formerly at the Metropolitan Museum, where the traits become harsher and a graphic accentuation emerges reminiscent of Bartolo di Fredi and Francesco di Vannuccio according to stylistic principles similar to those followed in the workshop of Cristoforo di Bindoccio-Meo di Pero.[16]

Daniela Parenti

1) B. Berenson, *A Sienese Little Master in New York and Else-where*, in Art in America, VI, no. 2, 1918, p. 70, fig. 2.

2) B. Klesse, *Seidenstoffe in der italienischen Malerei des 14. Jahrhunderts*, Bern 1967, pp. 405-408.

3) G. Kaftal, *Iconography of the Saints in Tuscan Painting*, Florence 1952, cc. 4-8, 601-604.

4) *Ibidem*, cc. 36-37.

5) G. De Nicola, *Studi dell'Arte Senese*, 'Rassegna d'Arte', VI, 1919, p. 100; U. Gnoli, *Pittori e miniatori nell'Umbria*, Spoleto 1923, p. 86.

6) R. van Marle, *The Development of Italian Schools of Painting*, The Hague, V, 1925, p. 106 note 2.

7) G. Kaftal, *Iconography* cit., p. XXIII, no. 17; F. Zeri, Book review: P. Torriti, *La Pinacoteca Nazionale di Siena. I dipinti dal XII al XV secolo*, 'Antologia di Belle Arti', II, 1978, p. 151.

8) G. Freuler, *Manifestatori delle cose miracolose. Arte italiana del Trecento e del Quattrocento da collezioni in Svizzera e nel Liechtenstein*, exh. cat. (Thyssen Bornemisza Foundation 1991), Einsiedeln 1991, cat. 22.

9) F. Zeri, Book review cit., p. 151.

10) M. Tamassia, *Collezioni d'arte tra Ottocento e Novecento: Jacquier fotografi a Firenze, 1870-1935*, Naples 1995, p. 95, cat. 50840; E. Fahy, *The Master of the Richardson Tabernacle*, 'Arte Cristiana', XCVI, 2008, pp. 171-180.

11) A. De Marchi, in G. Sarti, *Trente-trois primitifs italiens de 1310 à 1500 du sacré au profane*, London 1998, p. 79 no. 15.

12) C. Volpe, in Matthiesen, *Early Italian Paintings and Works of Art 1300-1480*, London 1983, pp. 31-32, cat. 15.

13) S. Chiodo, in M. Boskovits, *Dipinti italiani del XIV e XV secolo. La collezione Crespi nel Museo Diocesano di Milano*, ed. M. Boskovits, Geneva 2000, p. 62.

14) E. Fahy, *The Master of the Richardson Tabernacle* cit.

15) *Idem, Iniziali miniate e tavolette di Biccherna. Studi recenti sul "dipingere in miniatura"*, 'Arte Cristiana', LXXIII, 1985, pp. 327-338, particularly p. 337, n. 13, no. 38.

16) S. Padovani, *Sulla traccia di Cristoforo di Bindoccio e Meo di Pero*, 'Bollettino d'Arte', 1982, 15, pp. 85-98; eadem, *Un aggiornamento del catalogo di Cristoforo di Bindoccio e Meo di Pero*, in *Opere e giorni. Studi su mille anni di arte europea dedicati a Max Seidel*, eds. K. Bergdolt, G. Bonsanti, Venice 2001, pp. 223-230.

Bibliography:

B. Berenson, *A Sienese Little Master in New York and Elsewhere*, in *Art in America*, VI, 1918, pp. 70-71, 81

G. De Nicola, *Studi dell'Arte Senese*, 'Rassegna d'Arte', VI, 1919, p. 99

U. Gnoli, *Pittori e miniatori nell'Umbria*, Spoleto 1923, p. 85

R. van Marle, *The Development of Italian Schools of Painting*, The Hague, V, 1925, pp. 100-106

G. Kaftal, *Iconography of the Saints in Tuscan Painting*, Florence 1952, p. XXIII, no. 17

E. Benezit, *Dictionnaire critique et documentaire des peintres, sculpteurs, dessinateurs et graveurs*, Paris 1976, II, p. 570

F. Zeri, Book review: P. Torriti, *La Pinacoteca Nazionale di Siena. I dipinti dal XII al XV secolo*, 'Antologia di Belle Arti', II, 1978, p. 151

C. Volpe, in Matthiesen, *Early Italian Paintings and Works of Art 1300-1480*, London 1983, pp. 31-32, cat. 15

M. Tamassia, *Collezioni d'arte tra Ottocento e Novecento: Jacquier fotografi a Firenze, 1870-1935*, Naples 1995, p. 95, cat. 50840

A. De Marchi, in G. Sarti, *Trente-trois primitifs italiens de 1310 à 1500 du sacré au profane*, London 1998, p. 79, n. 15

Semenzato, *Eredi Carlo De Carlo*, Florence, 11.6.2003, cat. 21

D. Parenti, in *Le opere del ricordo. Opere d'arte dal XIV al XVI secolo appartenute a Carlo De Carlo, presentate dalla figlia Lisa*, ed. A. Tartuferi, Florence 2007, pp. 20-23, cat. 2 (from which this entry is taken)

E. Fahy, *The Master of the Richardson Tabernacle*, 'Arte Cristiana', XCVI, 2008, pp. 171-180

R. van Marle, *La scuola pittorica orvietana del '300*, 'Bollettino d'Arte', XVII, 1923-1924, p. 331 note 20.

Rossello di Jacopo Franchi

Florence, ca. 1376-1456

10. Virgin and Child in Glory between Saint Paul, Saint John the Baptist, Saint Bartholomew the Apostle and Saint Catherine of Alexandria

Tempera on panel, 138 x 62 cm (54 $^1/_3$ x 24 $^2/_5$ in.), painted surface 92 x 44 cm (36 $^1/_4$ x 17 $^1/_3$ in.)
Inscription: "AVE MARIA GRA"

Provenance:
Private collection

The panel represents the Virgin in glory sitting on a cushion.[1] With her left hand she holds the Child, standing on her knees, while with her right hand she holds his foot. On the grass at the sides are two pairs of saints: clockwise, Saint Paul, Saint John the Baptist, Saint Bartholomew the Apostle and Saint Catherine of Alexandria. The Child, wearing a red garment,[2] makes a blessing gesture with his right hand and in his left hand holds the globe.[3] Saint Paul holds a sword in his right hand and a book in his left.[4] Saint John the Baptist is dressed in the traditional camel's hair and in his left hand holds a thin cruciform staff and a scroll bearing the inscription 'ECE AGN'.[5] Saint Bartholomew, with a traditional bearded face, holds a knife in his right hand and a book in his left.[6] Saint Catherine holds the palm of martyrdom in her right hand and the spiked wheel in her cloaked left hand.[7] At the bottom, in the centre of the composition, stands a vase,[8] gilded and punched with white lilies and roses, resting on grassy ground dotted with small flowers.

The gold background has incisions in the form of rays, covering the entire surface, which depart from the celestial vision. Standing out on the gold ground is the red of two cherubs on either side of the Virgin, while at the bottom in the centre a third cherub with splayed wings holds up the cloud supporting the group of the Virgin and Child. The roundel in the centre of the pinnacle represents the God the Father Blessing who in his cloaked left hand holds an open book with the initials Alpha and Omega.[9]

The carpentry, entirely original, has racemes in pastiglia at the top and a mixtilinear upper profile, a recurrent shape in Florentine panels during the first three decades of the Quattrocento.[10] On each side of the panel are three twisted columns, and, at either end of the inscription punched onto the base, two shields in relief. The latter were prepared to be painted with the coats-of-arms of two families. This type of personalization of the carpentry for the patrons who commissioned the work, associated with the union of two families in marriage,[11] would appear not to have been completed since there are no visible traces of colour on the shields.

The panel, recently restored (2001), is in good state of preservation. The glue joint which connected, since its origin, the two vertical boards forming the support separated in the upper part generating a fissure visible on the front face for the whole height of the pinnacle. Providing evidence of a previous undocumented intervention are two nailed iron platbands each terminating in a hinge eye which were added in order to attach the panel to the wall by means of two lateral hooks. Also, for the fixing to the wall, there is the little ring at the top.

Nothing is known about the provenance of this very fine little altarpiece, hitherto unpublished. The style reveals the hand of Rossello di Jacopo Franchi.[12] This is evident not only in the physiognomic types, an authentic hallmark of this painter, but also in the solid and very refined pictorial technique, which is perceptible in the elegant rendering of the drapery, the luminous colours laid over each other in subtle *velature*, the meticulous attention paid to the gilding and punching of the halos and to decorative details – the rings on the fingers of the Virgin, the design of the fabric of her clothes and the cushion, the white lilies on the vase, and the sandals of Saint John the Baptist. The combination of these factors confers to the images that agreeable and precious aspect which evidently intrigued Rossello's patrons, for whom his painting, characterized by considerable technical quality,[13] represented a conservative cultural choice and a safe economic investment.

Panels like this, in 15th-century terminology, were called '*colmi*', that is, small panels designed for personal devotion of dimensions that were suitable for domestic environments. In the workshops they were available both finished and semi-finished, in the latter case ready to be personalized for clients. Besides the above-mentioned possibility of painting family's coats of arms, personalization could take place with the addition of those saints corresponding to the names of secular patrons, or important saints for the religious order in the case of religious patrons.[14] In the Portate al Catasto of 1427 presented by the *compagnia* of Rossello and his brother Giunta, we read:"Abiamo tante merchantantie, di cholmicielli e tavolette inbastite, di valutta di fiorini quindici".[15] Again in the tax declarations of 1430 and 1433 the brothers declared the possession of semi-finished works for a similar value in florins.[16]

The rarity of the surviving original carpentry of this painting is accompanied by another rather unusual fact. The existence of a matching carpentry, comparable in size, of another panel painted by Rossello with a similar subject, the only differences being the depicted Saints and the figures of the roundels. I refer to the painting in Barcelona, at the Museu Nacional d'Art de Catalunya, representing the *Virgin and Child in Glory between Saint James, Saint John the Baptist, Saint Paul and a Bishop Saint (Augustine?)* with *God the Father Blessing* in the roundel of the pinnacle and *Saint Anthony Abbot* in the roundel under the base, the latter element completing the frame at the bottom (Fig. 1).[17]

The great skill and meticulousness of execution, together with the reiteration, for decades, of some compositional schemes, were typical of this industrious and well-established workshop. The figurative repertoire used, firmly rooted in the Florentine tradition, was a guarantee of commercial success. As well as the obvious analogies between the compositions of Barcelona and the painting presented here, single types were freely reproposed in different works by the painter. The figure of Saint John the Baptist who with his right hand indicates leftward towards the Child recurs in both works, and altogether about a dozen times in the painter's known artistic production.[18] The figure of the Child holding the globe with his left hand and blessing with his right hand occurs also in the Madonna of unknown location formerly part of the private collection of Vittorio Cini in Venice,[19] in that which in 1999 was in this same gallery[20] and in that of the Courtauld Institute in London.[21]

Various figures of similar appearance are encountered both in the paintings and in the miniatures ascribable to Rossello. The God the Father Blessing in the pinnacle of this altarpiece, for example, recalls the softly modelled one appearing in a decorated B initial ascribable to Rossello, to date unpublished and of unknown location. It represents the *God the Father Blessing and King David* and I know it only through this photographic representation of 1936, when it was at Perugia, part of the collection of the Belgian art historian Raimond van Marle (Fig. 2).[22] The composition and style of the figures, like the foliage decorating the body of the letter, are comparable with the illuminations of the Gradual D of Santo Stefano in Prato; documented payments for the work link the writing to the Florentine stationer

1. Rossello di Jacopo Franchi
Virgin and Child in Glory between Saint James, Saint John the Baptist,
Saint Paul and a Bishop Saint; God the Father Blessing (pinnacle),
Saint Anthony Abbot (base)
Barcelona, Museu Nacional d'Art de Catalunya

Calderino di Francesco,[23] the borders to Matteo Torelli and the illuminations to Rossello, between 1428 and 1429.[24] With regards to a possible provenance for this initial, I would mention the payment in 1431 to Rossello by the Compagnia del Bigallo for the execution "più tempo fa" of figures for an Antiphonal, lost following a flood of the River Arno, and the payment to Matteo Torelli for the borders of the same Antiphonal, dating to 1429.[25] Adherence to certain figurative choices makes dating the works of Rossello an arduous task. For the work presented here, the spacing between the figures of the Saints and the fixed-

2. Rossello di Jacopo Franchi
God the Father Blessing and King David Playing a Psaltery in an initial B
Private collection

ness of their poses, as well as the slackened rhythms of the composition, refer to the works belonging to the mature artistic activity of Rossello di Jacopo of the beginning of the fourth decade of the Quattrocento. This decade started for the painter with the 1431 payment from the Compagnia del Bigallo, to which the former van Marle initial is probably referrable, and ended with the *Coronation of the Virgin* of the Pinacoteca Nazionale di Siena. The latter, the central element of a dismembered triptych, signed and dated 1439,[26] represents a late revision by the painter, by this time sixty-three years of age, of the scheme of the previous, monumental version now in the Galleria dell'Accademia in Florence.

Elisa Camporeale

1) The prototype for the model of the Madonna sitting on clouds amid Saints is considered to be the altarpiece by Spinello Aretino of the Museum of Fine Arts di Springfield (Mass.), dated by Luciano Bellosi before 1390, see L. Bellosi, *Da Spinello Aretino a Lorenzo Monaco*, 'Paragone', 187, 1965, pp. 18-43, particularly p. 39. Millard Meiss considers this model the celestial version of the Madonna of Humility, sitting on a cushion raised above the ground. This choice would derive from the principle of antithesis which was widespread in Christian thought, according to which humility implies sublimity, see M. Meiss, *The Madonna of Humility*, 'Art Bulletin', 18, 1936, pp. 435-464, particularly pp. 447-448, and *idem, Painting in Florence and Siena after the Black Death. The Arts, Religion and Society in the Mid-Fourteenth Century*, New York 1951, pp. 132-156, particularly pp. 139, 145-156.

2) The clothes of the Child are of a priestly type. In the Epistle to the Hebrews, and in particular in chapters 2:14-18, and 5:5-6, Paul makes reference to Jesus as the high priest before God, made like unto his brethren, the initiator of a new cult of which he is the highest and eternal priest. For a commentary on the texts in which Christ is indicated as a high priest, see C. Cecchelli, *Mater Christi*, II, Rome 1948, pp. 94-97.

3) The representation of the universe as a sphere was widespread over the centuries, see G. Schiller, *Ikonographie der christlichen Kunst*, III, Gütersloh 1971, p. 176.

4) On the iconography of the Apostle of the people, see G. Kaftal, *Iconography of the Saints in Tuscan Painting*, Florence 1952, coll. 784-789, and *Bibliotheca Sanctorum*, X, Rome 1968, coll. 164-227.

5) See Joh 1:29, "Ecce agnus Dei, qui tollit peccatum mundi". In Mat 3:4 it is said that John's clothes were made of camel's hair, that he had a leather belt around his waist and that his food was locusts and wild honey; he is therefore often represented as an ascetic hermit in the desert, emaciated, and with a beard and long hair. See G. Kaftal, *Iconography* cit., coll. 549-560, and *Bibliotheca Sanctorum*, VI, Rome 1965, coll. 599-623.

6) On the attributes of the book and the knife of Saint Bartholomew, see G. Kaftal, *Iconography* cit., coll. 137-140, and *Bibliotheca Sanctorum*, II, Rome 1962, coll. 852-878.

7) On the iconography of Saint Catherine, the daughter of Queen Sabinella of Egypt, see G. Kaftal, *Iconography* cit., Florence 1952, num. 62 on pp. 226-234, *Bibliotheca Sanctorum*, III, Rome 1963, coll. 955-975, and L. Réau, *Iconographie de l'Art Chrétien*, III/I, Paris 1958, pp. 262-272.

8) The vase has been an element in Christian iconology since the earliest times; in litanies the vase is sometimes named in the place of Mary, a metaphor for her divine breast, the receptacle of Christ, see F. Quinterio, *Natura e architettura nella bottega robbiana. Vasi rappresentati e vasi veri*, in *I Della Robbia e l'arte nuova della scultura invetriata*, exh. cat. (Fiesole), ed. G. Gentilini, Florence 1998, p. 68.

9) Alpha and Omega are the letters that symbolize Christ as eternal hope, the Beginning and the End as in the verses of the Apocalypse 1:8, 21:6 and 22:13; see D. A. Covi, *The Inscription in Fifteenth Century Florentine Painting*, Ph. D. dissertation, New York University, I, 1958, pp. 82-83, and G. Schiller, *Ikonographie der christlichen Kunst*, III, Gütersloh 1971, pp. 170-171.

10) The mixtilinear upper profile had already appeared in some small altarpieces by Bernardo Daddi. In the works of Rossello, we find it for example in the triptych of the Museo Civico in Pistoia, probably completed by Rossello after the death of Mariotto di Nardo (ante 1424), in the small altarpiece of Barcelona (Fig. 1), and in the *Coronation of the Virgin* of the Galleria dell'Accademia in Florence. In architecture this shape appears in some buildings by Ghiberti and is sometimes referred to a Ghibertian; cf. A. De Marchi, *La pala d'altare. Dal paliotto al polittico gotico*, Florence 2009, p. 170.

11) To cite an example, coats-of-arms belonging to the Velluti and Baldovini Rinucci families appear at the base of the small twisted columns of the small altarpiece by Starnina dating from the very early years of the 15th century, formerly in the Carlo De Carlo collection; see A. Tartuferi, *Gherardo di Jacopo, Madonna col Bambino fra sei Santi e quattro angeli*, in *Un tesoro rivelato. Capolavori della Collezione Carlo De Carlo*, exh. cat. (Florence), eds. M. Scalini, A. Tartuferi, Florence 2001, p. 54, pl. XII. For further information on the style of this painter, who returned to Florence from Spain some time before the beginning of 1402, and on this painting, see D. Parenti, *Intorno a Lorenzo Monaco. Cenni sulla pittura fiorentina tardogotica*, in *Lorenzo Monaco: dalla tradizione giottesca al Rinascimento*, exh. cat. (Florence), eds. A. Tartuferi, D. Parenti, Florence 2006, pp. 67-74, particularly pp. 68-70.

12) Rossello di Jacopo, painter, illuminator and chestmaker, lived and worked in Florence, together with his younger brother Giunta. His enrolment in the Guild of Physicians and Apothecaries dates, in all probability, to 1397 and in that of the Woodcarvers to 1435. From 1410 the families of the two brothers rented from the Bigallo two mezzanines in Palazzo dei Cerchi, at number 1 Vicolo dei Cerchi, a short distance from the workshop, for which they were tenants of the Rinuccini family, on the ground floor of Palazzo Rinuccini, in Piazza dei Cerchi at number 1. Giunta, whose enrolment in the Compagnia di San Luca in 1424 is documented, was declared dead in 1442. Rossello made his will in 1450 and died of old age in 1456; he was buried in San Lorenzo. For a chronological list of documents concerning him and the signed and documented works, see W. Jacobsen, *Die Maler von Florenz zu Beginn der Renaissance*, Munich and Berlin 2001, pp. 625-627, 652 pls. 85, 86, 93. On Rossello I would also mention a doctorate thesis from the now far-off 1981, and, from more recent times, a proposed attribution of two angels painted on the back of a triptych of the Embriachi workshop at the Museo del Bargello; see C. T. Peters, *Rossello di Jacopo Franchi: Portrait of a Florentine Painter, ca. 1376-1456*, Ph. D. dissertation, Indiana University, 1981; M. Tomasi, *Angeli per gli Embriachi*, in *Nuovi studi sulla pittura tardogotica. Intorno a Lorenzo Monaco. Atti del convegno* (Fabriano-Foligno-Florence 2006), eds. D. Parenti, A. Tartuferi, Livorno 2007, pp. 168-175, particularly pp. 171-172; *idem, Bottega degli Embriachi e Pittore fiorentino (Bottega di Rossello di Jacopo Franchi?). Trittico. Madonna col Bambino, la Crocifissione, due apparizioni di Cristo, sante, santi e angeli. Firenze, primo quarto del XV secolo*, in *L'eredità di Giotto. Arte a Firenze 1340-1375*, exh. cat. (Florence), ed. A. Tartuferi, Florence 2008, pp. 164-165.

13) Technical perfection was the prime requisite sought after in any artistic manufacture. This criterion was still valid for a patron like Lorenzo il Magnifico; see C. Gilbert, *L'arte del Quattrocento nelle testimonianze coeve*, Florence-Vienna 1988, p. 150.

14) On the typology of '*colmi*', see V. Schmidt, *Painted Piety. Panel Painting for Personal Devotion in Tuscany, 1250-1400*, Florence 2005, pp. 205-212. On the secular patronage of this type of small altarpiece, see J. K. Lydecker, *Il patriziato fiorentino e la committenza artistica per la casa*, in *I ceti dirigenti nella Toscana del Quattrocento. Atti del V e VI convegno* (Florence 1982, 1983), Florence 1987, pp. 209-221.

15) The Portate al Catasto pertaining to Rossello from 1427 have been partly published in C. Pini, G. Milanesi, *La scrittura degli artisti italiani (secoli XIV-XVII)*, Florence 1876, num. 28.

16) Samples of Rossello's Declarations from 1430 and 1433 have been summarized in M. Levi D'Ancona, *Miniatura e miniatori a Firenze dal XIV al XVI secolo*, Florence 1962, p. 235.

17) The Barcelona panel (inv. MNAC/MAC 15932) measures 166 x 65 cm and was donated to the museum in 1919; it came

from the collection of the painter Claudí Sugrañes Lorenzale (1816-1889), an artist with an Italian father, pupil of Overbeck and resident in Rome between 1836 and 1844. For brief notes on the painting see M. Olivar, *Museu de arte de Cataluña*, Barcelona 1964, p. 151; *Gothic, art guide*, Barcelona 2000, pp. 65, 247.

18) The pose he assumes with the cross and scroll in the left hand and the right hand indicating the Saviour, very common in Florentine painting of the first three-quarters of the 15th century, corresponds, according to Dario Alessandro Covi, to a passage of the two hundred and eighty-third sermon of Saint Augustine; see D. A. Covi, *The Inscription in Fifteenth Century Florentine Painting* cit., pp. 41-42.

19) The former Cini panel, like the Barcelona panel illustrated here, have been attributed to an assistant of Rossello; see C. T. Peters, *Rossello di Jacopo Franchi* cit., pp. 293-294, 298-299, 304, fig. 50. I consider anachronistic Carol Peters' division into works "by Rossello", by an "assistant" and even by "school". Entrusting the execution of entire paintings or parts of paintings to companions, assistants and apprentices was common working practice in artistic workshops at this time, but this did not mean that the work was not recognized as autographic. The signature of the workshop master on works and his name on documents and contracts were representative of the whole group that worked with him, including, in the case of Rossello, his brother Giunta, a shadowy figure given that we know he was for a long time active at his elder brother's side though no work is actually ascribable to him with any certainty.

20) See E. Camporeale, *Rossello di Jacopo Franchi. Madonna col Bambino in trono fra San Giacomo Maggiore e San Giovanni Battista*, in *Moretti. Da Bernardo Daddi a Giorgio Vasari*, ed. M. P. Mannini, Florence 1999, pp. 88-93.

21) On the London painting, see P. Troutman, *The Painting Collections of the Courtauld Institute of Art*, Chicago/London 1979, p. 11.

22) The attribution may originate with Bernard Berenson, given that the photo is under the name of Rossello in his photo archive at Villa I Tatti. Indicative of the style of Rossello, in addition to the physiognomic typology of God the Father, of more elegant execution than the intoning king, are also the deep folds and the nervous movements of the slender fingers.

23) In the payments it is specified that the stationer Calderino was Florentine. I assume it was Domenico and Calderino di Francesco, who at the end of the second decade of the 15th century rented a workshop from the Badia Fiorentina, in the area of present-day Via della Condotta; see A. Guidotti, *Indagini su botteghe di cartolai e miniatori a Firenze nel XV secolo*, in *La miniatura italiana tra gotico e rinascimento. Atti del II Congresso di Storia della Miniatura Italiana* (Cortona 1982), II, Florence 1985, pp. 473-507, particularly p. 484.

24) The manuscript, housed at the Museo dell'Opera del Duomo in Prato, is the subject of a monograph; see V. Pieroni, *Un tesoro miniato. Il Graduale D dell'antica pieve di Santo Stefano a Prato*, Prato 2009.

25) These payments by the Compagnia del Bigallo have been transcribed respectively in M. Levi D'Ancona, *Miniatura e miniatori a Firenze* cit., pp. 191, 236.

26) On the Siena panel, see P. Torriti, *La Pinacoteca Nazionale di Siena. I dipinti dal XII al XV secolo*, Genoa 1977, pp. 409-410, fig. 491.

LIPPO D'ANDREA

Florence, 1377-ca. 1450

11. Saint Dominic

Tempera on panel, 82 x 42.8 cm (32 ¼ x 16 ⅘ in.), painted surface 77.5 x 39.5 cm (30 ¼ x 15 ¼ in.)

Provenance:
USA, private collection
Florence, Carlo De Carlo collection
Florence, Lisa De Carlo collection

Saint Dominic is represented according to the more typical iconography, with the white robe and black mantle that distinguished the monks who took their name from him, with the lily, the symbol of his purity of soul,[1] and with the book alluding to the rule of the Dominican order of which he was the founder. The figure is cut to three quarters of its overall height and must have constituted the right-hand panel of a triptych or pentaptych with the Virgin and Child in the centre.

For this painting we know of various passages on the art market: when it was part of an American private collection, on 9 January 1980, it appeared at a Sotheby's auction (Park Bernet) in New York already with an attribution to the Pseudo-Ambrogio di Baldese; subsequently it entered the De Carlo collection in Florence.

The painting as a whole is in a fine state of preservation. On its surface are three moderately noticeable cracks which have been filled and repainted: in line with the saint's right eye; to the side of his neck, running vertically; and running vertically from where the two lengths of the saint's mantle meet, through the codex, down to the lower edge of the painting. A final and more substantial filling, about two centimetres high, runs along the lower edge of the panel. The painting still has the punching incised on the gold along three of its edges, and conserves most of its gold background, which only in the upper area appears to have been covered by a recent intervention. There is an impoverishment of the pictorial matter beside the long stem of the lily held by the saint. The panel has been fixed onto a parquet support and shows, on the front side, part of the bare wood, devoid of any paint or preparation, which must have been covered by the frame and on which are visible the holes of two large nails that were almost certainly used to attach a cross-piece.

For a long time the hand of the prolific Lippo d'Andrea, a Florentine painter active between 1395 and 1440 and for long known as the Pseudo-Ambrogio di Baldese, has been recognized in this painting – by Federico Zeri, with an annotation on the photo of the painting kept at the scholar's Fototeca (Fig. 3), today in Bologna at the Foundation named after him, and by Miklós Boskovits, with an annotation on the photo preserved at the Frick Art Reference Library of New York.

The first scholar to take an interest in one of the works of this master, by publishing it, was Osvald Sirén, who in 1909 linked a triptych preserved in the Jarves collection of New Haven (today in the deposits of the Yale Art Gallery, Fig. 1) with the name of Ambrogio di Baldese, a Florentine master with a somewhat evanescent profile, to whom were attributed various fragments of the decoration of the Loggia del Bigallo.[2] Some years later Raimond van Marle

1. Lippo d'Andrea
Virgin and Child with Saints
New Haven, Yale Art Gallery

coined the critical name-tag of Pseudo-Ambrogio, pointing out that the artist of the triptych at Yale could not have been a painter of the generation of the real Ambrogio di Baldese, who was enrolled in the Guild of Physicians and Apothecaries in 1372 and was mentioned in documents above all as the assistant of Niccolò di Pietro Gerini.[3] A further, and not very fruitful attempt to give an identity to this master was made by Georg Pudelko who, after adding various other paintings to his list of works on the basis of stylistic similarities, proposed the name of Bonaiuto di Giovanni, an artist known only from archive documents.[4] After some thirty years in which no further interest was shown, the critical problem of Pseudo-Ambrogio again became the object of study following the Exhibition of Sacred Art at Certaldo in 1963. In the year of the exhibition two different reviews, written by Federico Zeri and Carlo Volpe, examined the case of the anonymous painter. Zeri's text attributed to him a considerable group of works,[5] while that by Volpe broke up the substantial corpus of paintings collected over the years, attributing some of them to different hands.[6] In the meantime, although the problem of the artist's historical and anagraphical identity remained unsolved, the list of his works grew in size to the point of reaching an exceptional number for a painter of the 15th century. They were for the most part small painted panels or altarpieces destined for domestic devotion, often preserved in private collections, or otherwise more demanding paintings, even though fragmentary, present in foreign museum collections and attributed to the Pseudo-Ambrogio through written correspondence especially by Boskovits and

2. Lippo d'Andrea
Saint Jerome
Krakow, Czartoryski Museum

3. Lippo d'Andrea
Saint Dominic
Cat. 11

Everett Fahy. Enzo Carli[7] subsequently attempted to identify the artist as Ventura di Moro, although this too proved unconvincing. Finally, a new area of study was opened up by the research of Serena Padovani,[8] who identified Pseudo-Ambrogio di Baldese as the painter of the frescoes representing *Stories of the Passion* that were rediscovered by Ugo Procacci in the Cappella Nerli of the Florentine church of Santa Maria del Carmine, executed in the year 1402 (according to a Carmelite source dated 1689), and mentioned by Vasari among the works of the so-called "Lippo fiorentino". Additional archive research carried out by Ugo Procacci ascertained that the anagraphical identity of the painter active at the church of the Carmine, and therefore Pseudo-Ambrogio, was to be identified as "Lippo d'Andrea di Lippo".[9] The documents of the Carmine do indeed refer laconically to a young man named Lippo, without specifying a family name, although a cross-check of the registers of the Physicians' and Apothecaries' Guild would confirm that persons named Lippo or Filippo active at the dawn of the 15th century were few in number, and of these only Lippo d'Andrea (born in 1377 and a member of the Guild in 1395) could have been considered young in 1402. In recent years further studies have sought to determine the chronology and clarify various lesser-known aspects of the youthly activity[10] and late production[11] of this artist.

The vast list of works by Lippo d'Andrea, including both frescoes, paintings on wood and even some miniatures,[12] suggests the existence of an active and well-structured workshop, one that was able over a period of about fifty years to bring to completion a large number of commissions, and around which other artists gravitated, such as Ventura di Moro, who was active some time between 1420 and 1480. Many fragments of dismembered polyptychs, some intact polyptychs, and various cycles of frescoes in the areas of Florence (castle of Vincigliata and church of the Carmine), Prato (Badia di Montepiano) and San Miniato (church of Santi Jacopo e Lucia) can in fact be attributed to Lippo and his assistants.

Lippo's artistic style traversed a number of different phases, each punctuated by the influence of more major artists. Initially he drew inspiration from Spinello Aretino, subsequently he was influenced by Agnolo Gaddi and Lorenzo Monaco, then later in the 1430s his style came close to that of Giovanni dal Ponte. The large number of works attributed to him is evidence of the popularity of his style, which nonetheless, starting from the third decade of the century, was requested by prevalently minor and no longer city-based patrons, revealing that Lippo's art had fallen behind the times, times now marked by the revolution of Masaccio's painting. Denying any sympathy for the innovative figurative models being established on the scaffolded walls of the Cappella Brancacci, Lippo d'Andrea ended his career toward the beginning of the 1440s, the period when the Land Registry records, no longer signed by him, began to bear beside his name the annotation "istassi a chasa". The artist died around the middle of the century, the time when his wife declared herself a widow.[13]

Within the compass of the extensive list of works by Lippo d'Andrea, the *Saint Dominic* presently under examination, as already acknowledged by Zeri (with an annotation on the photo of the painting housed at the Fototeca in Bologna) and Boskovits (with an opinion recorded on the back of the photo at the Frick Art Reference Library), has been related to

4. Lippo d'Andrea
Saint Peter Martyr (detail)
Castelfiorentino (Florence), church of Santi Biagio e Ippolito

another painting, representing *Saint Jerome* (Fig. 2), which originally was certainly part of the same altarpiece. The *Saint Jerome*, now kept at the Czartoryski Museum in Krakow, has in common with the *Saint Dominic*, not only the style, but also the size, the punching, and the presence of a band, at the top, which originally must have been covered by the frame. The Saint Jerome would have been positioned to the right of the Virgin, that is, on the opposite side to the Saint Dominic; the former also holds an open book bearing a long inscription, which reads "Beatus Ieronimus tantum favorem propter sacras litteras apud populum obte-nuit [*sic*] quod omnium iudicio summo sacerdotio dignus esset".[14]

The altarpiece to which both paintings belonged was in all probability destined for a convent of Dominican nuns, given the importance attributed to the figure of Jerome, the saint who had done so much to encourage female monasticism.[15] In the corpus of works attributed to Lippo, this dismembered altarpiece seems datable to the second half of the 1420s, a decade coinciding with the artist's interest in the style of Lorenzo Monaco, which starts with the triptych now at the Yale Art University (dated 1420) and ends with the *Pietà and Saints* (Fig. 4) frescoed in the church of Santi Biagio e Ippolito at Castelfiorentino (dated 1429).[16] The *Saint Dominic*, with the striking linearistic definition of the cowl of the mantle, recalls above all the flowing yet subdued rhythms of the figures of saints in the splays of the Castelfiorentino tabernacle (Fig. 4), while other touches, like the use of hatching on the white, or the intensely chiaroscuro rendering of the saint's face, are fairly typical of the artist. The three-quarter length of the figure appears not infrequently in the work of Lippo; it can be seen, for example, in a triptych recently recomposed by Sonia Chiodo and once on the altar of the Blessed Davanzato da Poggibonsi in the church of Santa Lucia at San Casciano near Barberino Val d'Elsa. It is this work indeed that would suggest that the polyptych containing the panel described here was also once completed by a predella with narrative scenes.[17]

Linda Pisani

1) An attribute that appears from the beginning of the Trecento, cf. G. Kaftal, *Iconography of the Saints in Tuscan Painting*, Florence 1952, coll. 309-319.

2) O. Sirén, *Trecento Pictures in American Collections, III*, 'The Burlington Magazine', XIV, 1909, p. 326.

3) R. van Marle, *The Development of Italian Schools of Painting*, The Hague, III, 1924, p. 612, and IX, 1927, pp. 86-92.

4) G. Pudelko, *The Minor Masters of the Chiostro Verde*, 'The Art Bulletin', 1935, pp. 83-89.

5) F. Zeri, *La mostra "Arte Sacra in Valdelsa" a Certaldo*, 'Bollettino d'Arte', III, 1963, 24, pp. 247-248 and pp. 256-257 note 8.

6) C. Volpe, *Recensione a Arte in Valdelsa dal secolo XII al secolo XVIII*, 'Arte Antica e moderna', XXIV, 1963, p. 390.

7) E. Carli, *Chi è lo "pseudo Ambrogio di Baldese"?*, in *Studi in onore di Valerio Mariani*, 1971, pp. 109-112, plates LV-LVI, figs. 1-2.

8) S. Padovani, *San Michele Arcangelo*, in *Tesori d'Arte antica a San Miniato al Tedesco*, Genoa 1979, pp. 55-57.

9) U. Procacci, *Lettera a Roberto Salvini con vecchi ricordi e alcune notizie su Lippo d'Andrea modesto pittore del primo Quattrocento*, in *Scritti di Storia dell'arte in onore di Roberto Salvini*, Florence 1984, pp. 213-226.

10) S. Chiodo, *Lippo d'Andrea: problemi di iconografia e stile*, 'Arte Cristiana', XC, 2002, 808, pp. 1-16.

11) L. Pisani, *Pittura tardogotica a Firenze negli anni trenta del Quattrocento: il caso dello pseudo-Ambrogio di Baldese*, 'Mitteilungen des Kunsthistorischen Institutes in Florenz', XLV, 2001, pp. 1-36.

12) For his activity as an illuminator see L. Pisani, *Lippo d'Andrea/Pseudo Ambrogio di Baldese*, in *Dizionario Biografico dei Miniatori*, ed. M. Bollati, Milan 2004, pp. 390-394.

13) U. Procacci, *Lettera a Roberto Salvini con vecchi ricordi e alcune notizie su Lippo d'Andrea modesto pittore del primo Quattrocento*, in *Scritti di Storia dell'arte in onore di Roberto Salvini*, Florence 1984, pp. 213-226.

14) The text of the inscription – in Gothic characters, with numerous abbreviations and the first letter in red – is not one of the passages that most frequently accompanies the saint (for which cf. G. Kaftal, *Iconography* cit., col. 523).

15) On the life and the role of Saint Jerome in relation to female monasticism cf. E. Rice, *St. Jerome in the Renaissance*, Baltimore 1985, *passim*.

16) On the latter cf. S. Chiodo, *Gli affreschi della chiesa di San Domenico a San Miniato: un capitolo poco noto della pittura fiorentina tra Trecento e Quattrocento (parte II)*, 'Arte Cristiana', XCVI, 2008, pp. 89-90 and p. 94 notes 52-57.

17) *Ibidem*, p. 90 and fig. 23.

Bibliography:
Old Masters Paintings, Sotheby's, Park Bernet, New York, 9.1.1980.

Mariano d'Angelo Romanelli (and Bartolo di Fredi?)

Siena, documented 1376-1410

12. The Christ Child Wrapped in Swaddling-Clothes

Polychromed and gilded wood, height 46 cm (18 $^1/_8$ in.)

Provenance:
Rome, private collection
Florence, Tammaro De Marinis collection
France, private collection

The rediscovery of this beautiful Trecento Sienese wooden sculpture of the newborn Christ Child wrapped in swaddling clothes is a fascinating addition to our knowledge of sculpture in Siena, which, as was demonstrated in the unforgettable and exemplary exhibition *Scultura Dipinta* held in 1987 in the Pinacoteca Nazionale di Siena,[1] in the last decades of the 14th century and in the 15th century enjoyed a period of remarkable prosperity. Artists like Mariano d'Angelo Romanelli, Magister Angelus (Angelo di Nalduccio), Domenico di Niccolò 'dei cori', and Francesco da Valdambrino paved the way for younger colleagues such as Jacopo della Quercia, who under the influence of the Florentine sculptors Donatello and Lorenzo Ghiberti set off to new shores of Renaissance art in Siena.[2]

It is to this context of later Trecento Sienese wooden sculptures that we should assign the charming 46 cm wooden statue. This little-known, finely carved polychrome sculpture was first published by Ursula Schlegel, who summarily assigned it to the Italian school of the 15th century.[3] At the time of its publication the sculpture was owned by the famous Florentine collector and art-dealer of Neapolitan origin, Tammaro De Marinis (1878-1969), who was particularly famed for his important collection of Italian illuminated manuscripts.

Freed from later repaint since Schlegel's publication, and despite some minor wear to the original polychromy, the otherwise well-preserved sculpture has maintained much of its original appearance and there can be no doubt that it was carved and painted by Sienese masters during the last quarter of the 14th century.

The present sculpture of the newborn Christ is clearly intended as a variation of an old prototype invented a good century earlier, presumably around 1260, by Nicola Pisano. Two such marble figures from his workshop have come down to us, one now in the Bargello in Florence and the other formerly in the Longari collection in Milan.[4] As has been demonstrated by Guido Tigler, these two marbles from Nicola Pisano's workshop might be based on an even earlier invention by Nicola Pisano himself, which has survived as a fragment in the Cistercian monastery of Sankt Marienstern in Saxony.[5]

Similar to later Sienese interpretations of the earlier 14th century, such as the wooden sculptures of the *Christ Child* by the so-called 'Master of the Madonna of Sant'Agostino a Perugia' (Figg. 1, 2, 3), formerly in the Bruera collection in Pisa and now in the Bargello,[6] by an anonymous artist, formerly in the De Carlo collection, and a third in the Bode Museum in Berlin, the Christ Child presented here maintains the rigid pose of the old model invented by Nicola Pisano as well as the facial structure with wide-open staring eyes and a small slightly open mouth. This rigidity is accentuated by the fact that in contrast to the older

models our Christ Child does not wear a tunic which falls with elegant folds, producing a graceful and ornate appearance, but is wrapped in the tightly adherent bandages of the swaddling cloths. Despite this difference compared to the older models, the retrospective adherence to old inventions, observed in our sculpture, distinguishes it from those produced in the early years of the 15th century by a later generation of Sienese sculptors including Domenico di Niccolò 'dei cori' (*Christ Child* in the Monte dei Paschi collection in Siena) and the anonymous sculptor who carved the *Christ Child* (Fig. 4) formerly in Santa Maria Aracoeli in Rome which was stolen from there in 1994.[7] In line with later Gothic tendencies in Tuscan art around 1400, the sculptors of these two works give their figures a new sense of movement and a dynamic twist, as well as a new more naturalistic texture in the articulation of the face. In the case of the sculpture by Domenico di Niccolò 'dei cori' in the collection of the Banca del Monte dei Paschi (Fig. 5), the bandages of the swaddling cloths are loosened by the Child's stirring, giving the impression that the Child wanted to free himself of his clothes and step out of them.

Despite the retrospective aspect of our figure, the art of its sculptor clearly reveals a certain late Trecento tendency toward naturalistic observation which also characterizes Mariano d'Angelo's wooden sculptures, created in the later 1380s,[8] including the little seated Christ Child in a private collection in Lugano (Fig. 6) which I had assigned to him in 1991.[9] But it

1., 2., 3. Master of the Madonna of Sant'Agostino a Perugia
Christ Child
Florence, Museo del Bargello

is not with those sculptures, presumably datable between 1380 and 1390, that we should associate this sculpture, but rather with works created slightly earlier, particularly those in marble commissioned to Romanelli in 1376 and 1378 for the new chapel of the Piazza del Campo and still visible today *in situ*. These large-scale figures placed in niches are a hardly surprising late Trecento homage to the greatest Sienese monumental sculptor Giovanni Pisano, who paved the way for such figures on the facade of the cathedral in Siena. It is in the same retrospective spirit, though within a more up-to-date artistic style, that our Christ Child is conceived, offering a more modern variation of Nicola Pisano's model created a century earlier. The mood of the finely-carved and well-articulated face of our Child compares to the mood expressed by the face of Saint James the Less in the Cappella del Campo. Despite the fact that they represent completely different figural types with different ages – one a newborn child, the other a young apostle – both figures share a similar slightly rigid emotion created by their rather fixed gaze, and even the composition of the elegant and harmoniously flowing locks is conceived in a comparably subtle manner.

If we agree with the attribution of this figure of the newborn Christ to the early activity of Mariano d'Angelo Romanelli, datable around the second half of the 1370s, then we might have an interesting lead on the painter who may have executed the statue's polychrome decoration.

4. Anonymous Sculptor
Christ Child
Rome, church of Santa Maria Aracoeli (stolen in 1994)

5. Domenico di Niccolò 'dei cori'
Christ Child
Siena, Monte dei Paschi di Siena collection

About twenty years ago, in the course of my research on the Sienese Trecento painter Bartolo di Fredi, I discovered a document that testified to a collaboration in 1385 between this painter and the sculptor in question, Mariano d'Angelo Romanelli, and confirmed an idea based on stylistic observation that Bartolo di Fredi was also responsible for the painting of the reliquary bust of Saint Ursula (Fig. 7) carved presumably in the later 1380s by our sculptor in the Musei Civici in San Gimignano.[10] This might point towards a well-established collaboration between these two artists for the production of painted wooden sculptures in the 1380s which may actually have started at an earlier time.

In 1374 Bartolo was chosen over his fellow painters by the sculptors' guild to paint their chapel in the cathedral of Siena.[11] Since in those years he was regarded by the Sienese sculptors as the best painter for their important project, we can surmise that some of their members, among them Mariano d'Angelo Romanelli, would also have selected him to paint their own statues. One might also wonder whether it was pure coincidence that some years later Mariano d'Angelo Romanelli was hired with other sculptors to supply the marble sculptures for the Cappella della Piazza outside the Palazzo Pubblico, for which, as will be discussed by Wolfgang Loseries and other co-authors in a forthcoming study,[12] in 1374 Bartolo di Fredi had furnished a project that, although not followed, has survived as a wonderful and detailed drawing in the Museo dell'Opera del Duomo in Siena. Thus, it may well be that the later documented collaboration between Bartolo di Fredi and Mariano d'Angelo Romanelli

6. Mariano d'Angelo Romanelli
Christ Child
Lugano, private collection

7. Mariano d'Angelo Romanelli
Saint Ursula
San Gimignano (Siena), Musei Civici

was the continuation of a partnership in this sector which might have started already as early as the 1370s.

It may well be, therefore, that the *Christ Child* under discussion was painted by Bartolo di Fredi. This might explain its characteristic subtly painted pink colouring which reappears on Romanelli's sitting Christ Child in a private collection in Lugano and on the above-mentioned reliquary bust of Saint Ursula in San Gimignano, which inside her crown bears a painted head of the Christ Child clearly by the hand of Bartolo di Fredi.[13]

The present wooden statue of the Christ Child, presumably carved by Mariano d'Angelo Romanelli and most probably coloured by Bartolo di Fredi around 1375, is an interesting addition to the series of such para-liturgical objects which in the course of the 14th century – and hand in hand with a more emphatic spirituality – enjoyed increasing popularity. A spirituality which suggested an emphatic contemplation of the life of Christ and Mary's motherhood as recommended with particular insistence in the milieu of the Franciscan order[14] – though not only in these circles – also evoked new para-liturgical rites, such as the display at Christmas time of carved wooden figures of the newborn Christ Child on the main altar or alternatively in a cradle in a chapel dedicated to the Virgin or to the mystery of the Nativity.

Rituals of this nature and objects produced specially for this purpose, such as painted wooden sculptures of the newborn Christ Child, are numerously documented in the 14th and 15th centuries throughout Europe and particularly in Tuscany, where towards the end of the 14th century in relation to the Sienese cathedral we repeatedly hear about such objects.[15]

The particular function of our small sculpture also explains why the artist chose not to place his wooden figure on a small pedestal in the shape of a cushion, as would have been expected for a figure placed on an altar (see for instance Romanelli's sitting Christ in Lugano), but leave the Child's feet free and have them carefully painted. The aim was to produce an object that, almost like a doll, could be handed to the faithful during the para-liturgical functions at Christmas and then be put back in a wooden cradle, in which it was held during Christmas time.[16]

Gaudenz Freuler

1) *Scultura Dipinta. Maestri di Legname e Pittori a Siena 1250-1450*, exh. cat. (Siena, Pinacoteca Nazionale, 16.7.-31.12.1987), Florence 1987.

2) *Da Jacopo della Quercia a Donatello. Le Arti a Siena nel primo Rinascimento*, exh. cat. (Siena, 26.3.-11.7.2010), Siena 2010.

3) U. Schlegel, *The Christchild as Devotional Image in Medieval Italian Sculpture: A Contribution to Ambrogio Lorenzetti Studies*, 'The Art Bulletin', 52, 1970, pp. 1-10.

4) G. Tigler, in *Spunti per conversare, Milan Galleria Longari, 10*, Milan 2007, pp. 17-27, figs. on pp. 18, 19 and 20.

5) *Ibidem*, p. 20 ff.; G. Kreytenberg, *Ein lehrender Christus von Nicola Pisano im Zisterzensierinnenkloster St. Marienstern in Sachsen*, 'Mitteilungen des Kunsthistorischen Institutes in Florenz', XLIII, 1999, pp. 1-12.

6) G. Previtali, *Due lezioni sulla scultura "umbra" del Trecento*, 'Prospettiva', 32, 1983, pp. 12-20.

7) G. Fattorini, in *Da Jacopo della Quercia a Donatello* cit., p. 292.

8) For Mariano d'Angelo Romanelli's artistic career see A. Bagnoli, in *Scultura Dipinta* cit., pp. 80-95.

9) G. Freuler, *"Künder der wunderbaren Dinge" Früher italienische Malerei aus sammlungen in der Schweiz und Liechtenstein*, exh. cat. (Lugano, Thyssen Foundation 1991), Lugano/Einsiedeln 1991, pp. 74-76.

10) G. Freuler, *Bartolo di Fredi Cini. Ein Beitrag zur sienesischen Malerei des 14. Jahrhunderts*, Disentis 1994, p. 272 ff. and p. 425, docs. 66, 67.

11) *Ibidem*, p. 419, doc. 25.

12) Newly found archival material from 1374 allowed Wolfgang Loseries and his collaborators to assign the celebrated detailed architectural drawing for the Cappella della Piazza (Museo dell'Opera del Duomo in Siena) to Bartolo di Fredi. This material was presented in the past by these scholars in various conferences and will shortly be the topic of an immi-

nent scholarly publication. I am grateful to Wolfgang Loseries for sharing his research with me.

13) Gaudenz Freuler (as in note 9), who challenges Alessandro Bagnoli's attribution to Bartolo di Fredi's son Andrea di Bartolo (A. Bagnoli, in *Scultura Dipinta* cit., pp. 83-85).

14) The basis for para-liturgical functions and mystery plays on the occasion of Christmas was certainly the legend of Saint Francis' Christmas mass at Greccio. Para-liturgical functions with wooden sculptures of the Christ Child might also have been suggested and popularized by meditational literature like the Franciscan *Meditationes Vitae Christi*, where the moment of the Birth of Christ is narrated with great emphasis on the human nature of Christ and encouragement in deep contemplation. After describing the adoration of the shepherds who knelt down to adore their newborn Saviour, the author of the *Meditationes* turns to the reader, inviting him to do the same as the shepherds: "...you too, who lingered so long, kneel and adore your Lord God, and then His mother and [...] Kiss the beautiful little feet of the infant Jesus who lies in the manger and beg his mother to offer to let you hold Him a while. Pick Him up and hold Him in your arms..." (*Meditations on the Life of Christ. An illustrated manuscript of the fourteenth century. Paris Bibliothèque Nationale MS. Ital 115*, eds. I. Ragusa, R. B. Green, Princeton 1961, p. 38).

15) G. Tigler cit., pp. 23-27, and J. Tripps, *Das handelnde Bildwerk in der Gotik*, Berlin 2002.

16) For an Italian painted cradle of a somewhat later period, towards the end of the 15th century and presumably used for such para-liturgical functions at Christmas, see fig. 36 in B. Zierhut-Bösch, *Ikonographie der Mutterschaftsmystik-Interpendenzen zwischen Andachtsbild und Spiritualität im Kontext spätmittelalterlicher Frauenmystik*, unpublished MA thesis (University of Linz), 2007.

Bibliography:

U. Schlegel, *The Christchild as Devotional Image in Medieval Italian Sculpture: A Contribution to Ambrogio Lorenzetti Studies*, 'The Art Bulletin', 52, 1970, pp. 1-10.

VERONESE PAINTER
ca. 1380-1390

13. Crucifixion and Annunciation

Tempera on panel, 67 x 49.8 cm (26 $^3/_8$ x 19 $^5/_8$ in.)

Provenance:
Florence, Lydia Pegger Amari collection (*ante* 1935)
Switzerland, private collection

The panel is made from two vertical pieces of wood that had come apart in the centre, where the support has been mended by grafting onto the back a reinforcement made from an old piece of wood. The most significant losses are in the area of this vertical crack, corresponding to the axis of the Cross, and particularly the ground at the feet of Mary Magdalen, though their retouching, following the recent restoration carried out by Loredana Gallo, is perfectly recognizable. The painted surface is generally well-preserved, apart from some deterioration of the gilding, for example on the disputed tunic of Christ, and the consumption of the gold background, which although marred by a geometrical 'graffito' on the right, still conserves the original incisions of the rays around the angels, fluidly and picturesquely painted. The application of a reconstructed and rather mediocre frame has involved regildings that bleed onto the background and extend into the pendentives with the Annunciation, as well as the probable sacrifice of parts of the original painting, as is suggested by the figure dressed in pink, on the far left, holding a stick, whose face, now covered, was probably meant to be seen.

The painting belonged to the Florentine collection of Lydia Pegger Amari, where it was photographed before 1935 by Vittorio Jacquier (1865-1935): the negative belongs to the Soprintendenza per il Polo Museale e i Beni Artistici della città di Firenze (neg. 50170) and was reproduced by Marilena Tamassia (1995), who attributed the work to the Abruzzo school of the 16th century, advancing comparisons also with the Salimbeni and with Ottaviano Nelli. The composition is constructed on three levels: in the foreground the mourners and to the right a group of soldiers disputing the clothes of Christ; behind them numerous figures on horseback, rising in a somewhat exaggerated fashion; in the upper part Christ between the thieves, the latter much smaller in comparison, and the lament of the angels. The disproportion of the three groups makes the scene even wilder and more picturesque. The idea of surging ranks of horsemen on the middle level derives from Giotto and was developed with a more accentuated and polyphonic arrangement in the *Calvaries* of the following neo-Giottesque Venetian painters: Altichiero (Padua, chapel of San Giacomo al Santo, 1376-1379, and oratory of San Giorgio, 1379-1384, Fig. 2), Giusto de' Menabuoi (Padua, Baptistery, ca. 1380) and Turone di Maxio (Verona, San Fermo Maggiore, counterfacade, ca. 1385, Fig. 4). The painter of the present panel was clearly influenced by these models, although his interpretation nonetheless is characterized by surprising vivacity and freedom. Various details clearly reveal this. For example, in the scene of the dispute over Christ's clothes we see not the purple mantle, as is traditional, but rather a white tunic decorated in gold, like

the one in the chapel of San Giacomo. The two thieves are hung with their arms twisted back behind the horizontal arm of the cross, exactly as in the oratory of San Giorgio, this being repeated by a follower in Santa Lucia at Treviso. Here, however, the realistic brutality is even more poignant: as at Padua the legs have already been broken, though the bodies, constrained by ropes (which Altichiero and Giusto leave out and which are lacking around the legs also in the examples of Rimini, Munich, Allentown, Ingenheim coll.), still appear to be flailing; the penitent thief kicks and one foot is acutely foreshortened, while the other thief turns away from Christ. The swooning of the Virgin, here shown falling into the arms of her companions, is an image deriving from Giotto that appears in a similar way in Turone, in the Second Master of San Zeno (Verona, San Giorgetto, 1353-1354) and in Giusto, while Mary Magdalen shown fervently embracing the base of the Cross and clasping a lock of her thick hair, as if wanting to reproduce the gesture with which she had anointed Christ's feet with perfume at the house of Levi, appeared in works of the early Trecento both from Rimini (Pietro da Rimini, Ravenna, Santa Chiara; Francesco da Rimini, Zurich, Kunsthaus) and Friuli (Cividale, San Francesco and San Giorgio at Rualis; veil of the Beata Boiani), as if to suggest a common Giottesque prototype (it was also used by Zanino di Pietro in Venice, in the triptych for Rieti, ca. 1407). Recurrent in Venetian neo-Giottism, and inspired by the Scrovegni chapel, is the representation of halos, here in particular that of a pious woman standing behind Mary Magdalen. The figure beating the legs of the bad thief with a stick is present in Giusto, and even before, around 1355, in the cycle of Sant'Orsola at Vigo di Cadore. Stephaton, the young soldier who offered Christ a sponge soaked in vinegar, here on the end of a knobbly cane, is often represented in Rimini and in the Veneto with an image

1. Reflectography of the *Crucifixion and Annunciation*
Cat. 13

2. Altichiero
Crucifixion
Padua, oratory of San Giorgio

3. Second Master of San Zeno (?)
Crucifixion
Verona, Museo di Castelvecchio (from Casa Bernasconi, San Paolo)

of complacent realism, barefoot and dressed in rags (in this painting he wears a curious jacket lined with rustic fur, torn on the back and showing a tuft of the lining). A horseman on the right raises his arm and points toward Christ; on his armour are two wings in silver that are repeated on his helmet, as is seen also in a detached fresco from Casa Bernasconi (Fig. 3), now at the Museo di Castelvecchio, probably a late work by the Second Master of San Zeno, now influenced by the younger Turone, to whom it had been erroneously attributed. In their Calvaries the three major artists we mentioned previously tried out their artistic skills in the almost individualized representation of the variously dappled steeds, preparing the way for the animalistic portraits of Pisanello: in this panel they are among the most successfully rendered images, with their simpering and somewhat affected expressions particularly reminiscent of Turone, some manes ruffled by the breeze and in one case even two touches of white to indicate a frothing mouth. The scene is remarkably animated as a result of the many heads popping up at the bottom, the variety of different gestures, and the frenetic interaction of the figures, with the wonderful touch of a horseman sounding a very long clarion held up above the nearby horses. The face of Stephaton is seen in profile, as in Altichiero, and another Altichieresque touch can be seen in the bearded soldier on the extreme right, whose upturned gaze is hidden by his helmet. Among the crowd we see a coloured man, as we do also in Turone (and even before at Vigo di Cadore, following the example of Giotto himself in the Scrovegni chapel, in Christ before Caiaphas). The soldiers do not throw dice for Christ's clothes, but draw straws, a rarer version spread by Vitale da Bologna in Friuli which is later found in Tuscany, in the works of Antonio Veneziano and Agnolo Gaddi. Finally, there is an iconographical detail I find quite astounding and for

4. Turone di Maxio
Crucifixion
Verona, San Fermo Maggiore

which I am unable to indicate similar cases. In these Venetian *Calvaries* Longinus is usually represented at the precise moment in which he finally recognizes Christ, his hands joined together in prayer, his lance resting on his shoulder or his hat lowered in reverence. Here instead he is portrayed in the act of piercing Christ's side with the lance, as in Giusto, yet with another touch of realism, for his blindness, which will be cured by the Saviour's spurting blood as a metaphorical image of his sudden conversion, is expressed by the bandage tied over his closed and swollen eyelids, and so another horseman behind him helps him to strike with the lance! The difficulty of spatially coordinating such a complex composition is thus balanced by the freshness of sharp, realistic details that can be admired at leisure, and whose description could continue at length.

Notwithstanding the artist's certain familiarity with the work of Altichiero, the painter is not a close follower of the latter; he reveals empirical limitations in the rendering of space and there is a slackness in the execution that suggests links with the previous period of Veronese painting, with Turone, and even with the legacy of painters of the first half of the century, like the First Master of San Zeno. The "Veronese-ness" seems to me to be confirmed by the Annunciation painted in the pendentives, which recalls Turone, but also in a precise way the above-mentioned fresco of Casa Bernasconi, relating to the final phase of the Second Master of San Zeno, where it occupied an identical position, on the frontispiece framing the arched scene of the *Crucifixion*. It is difficult to narrow the attribution to a precise stylistic group, but the context does seems to be precisely this one. We have, therefore, a fascinating example of the absorption of Venetian neo-Giottism on a substratum of sharper and more detailed expressiveness on the part of a master of secondary stature who was nonetheless capable of expressing himself with considerable verve. Veronese painting of the Trecento is familiar to us through a substantial number of frescoes; much rarer are the paintings on panel, a fact that prevents a more comprehensive description of this work yet at the same time makes it all the more praiseworthy.

Andrea De Marchi

Bibliography:
M. Tamassia, *Collezioni d'arte tra Ottocento e Novecento. Jacquier fotografi a Firenze 1870-1935*, Naples 1995, p. 23.

Martino di Bartolomeo

Siena, ca. 1365/1370-1435

14. Saint John the Baptist; *(in the trilobe of the upper register)* Angel of the Annunciation

Tempera on panel, 119 x 43 cm (46 $^7/_8$ x 17 in.)

Provenance:
Falzano (Cortona), parish church of Santa Maria
London, Colnaghi, 1991

The panel with the powerful kneeling Saint John the Baptist in adoration painted undoubtedly by the Sienese painter Martino di Bartolomeo is certainly the lateral section of a larger altarpiece which on the opposite side included a painting with the figure of Mary Magdalen, the whereabouts of which has remained unknown since Berenson's publication in 1968.[1] Although we do not know its size, there is no doubt that this Magdalen painted by Martino di Bartolomeo belonged with our panel to the same altarpiece, which, as we shall discuss, on the central panel represented the Assumption of the Virgin. Both lateral panels were conceived with a corresponding framing device and identical moulding, as well as with a matching iconography in the upper register, where above Saint John we find the Angel of the Annunciation and to the right, above Saint Mary Magdalen, the Virgin of the Annunciation. Both saints in the two lateral panels are shown kneeling down and are at the same time reverently turned towards an event painted on the central panel, to which they emphatically point with their right hand. When I first discussed these paintings in 1991, I hypothesized that the central panel might have shown the Trinity or a Crucifixion. In the meantime I have succeeded in solving the enigma by identifying the missing central panel as Martino di Bartolomeo's *Assumption of the Virgin* (132 x 54 cm) from the destroyed (1944) parish church of Falzano near Cortona, now in the Museo Diocesano in Cortona (Fig. 1).[2] The polilobe framing of the arch of this panel is congruent with what we see on the corresponding lateral panels and the traces of moulding belonging to the damaged and practically lost central trilobe which presumably contained a Blessing Christ is also consistent with the rest of this dismembered altarpiece.

From our reconstruction emerged an altarpiece of respectable dimensions (Fig. 2) with a width of 160-180 cm (including the now lost carpentry and the two lost lateral pilasters) and a height of about 160 cm (including the now lost or not yet identified predella).

Given that the parish church of Falzano was dedicated to the Virgin, we might reasonably surmise that this considerable altarpiece with the Triumph of the Virgin, her Assumption to Heaven on the central panel, may originally have stood on the high altar of this church. It is not known when the altarpiece was dismembered, though we have good reasons to believe that this happened long before the destruction of the church in 1944.

If we now attempt to establish an art historical assessment of this reunited altarpiece within Martino di Bartolomeo's career, there are some specific features of the painting which particularly deserve our attention. Here Martino di Bartolomeo conceived his figures in sculptural terms, particularly Saint John the Baptist, emphazing a sense of movement in a

1. Martino di Bartolomeo
Assumption of the Virgin (detail)
Cortona (Arezzo), Museo Diocesano

confined space. At the same time he imparted the appropriate spiritual energy to his figures with a careful naturalistic rendering of anatomical details, such as – a propos of the saint shown here – the sharply defined facial features, with wrinkles on the brow and protruding veins in the neck. This aspect seems to reflect the painter's particular affinity with several of Siena's leading sculptors of the early 15th century. We know from documents that his friendship with many of them (Domenico di Niccolò 'dei cori' and Jacopo della Quercia) was so close that they would become godfathers to some of his numerous children. Martino's close friendship with some leading sculptors resulted in a great number of commissions to paint the wooden sculptures carved by them.[3] Therefore it hardly comes as a surprise to see in Martino di Bartolomeo's works a special sensitivity toward the sculptural quality in the composition of his figures. These characteristics are traceable among works that were painted during the period when the artist had been well-established in Siena after a lengthy absence from his home town, when between the 1390s and the early years of the 15th century he focused on cosmopolitan activity with Pisan, Florentine and Neapolitan painters in the area of Pisa and Lucca. In the second half of the first decade of the 15th century he returned to Siena, where he quickly became one of the most successful and prolific painters. The style of the Falzano altarpiece is close to works that can be assigned to the second decade of the 15th century. The figure of our Saint John the Baptist can be linked to the same saint who appears in a similar pose in a fragmentary fresco of a *Maestà* (Fig. 3) formerly in the Compagnia di Sant'Ansano, now in the Università degli Studi di Siena, and more importantly to the frescoes of the *Trinity* in the then Ospedale di Santa Maria della Scala in Siena (ca. 1419). Here we observe Martino's same tendency to treat the human form in broad, monumental terms and to clothe his figures in abundant, elegantly flowing draperies that revealed a certain nostalgia for refined Gothic forms, which his contemporary Benedetto di Bindo had turned to, between 1409 and 1412, when he painted the frescoes for the sacristy of Siena cathedral, which with their Gothic elegance can be interpreted as a homage to Simone Martini, the former "prince of Sienese painting". In the first decade of the Quattrocento Benedetto di Bindo was probably the most elegant and talented Sienese painter active in that town, not inferior to the future protagonist Taddeo di Bartolo. Who knows what direc-

2. Martino di Bartolomeo
Reconstruction of the altarpiece
from the parish church of Falzano (Cortona)

tion he might have given to early Quattrocento art in Siena had he not been the victim of an untimely death in 1417? Together with Taddeo di Bartolo and Spinello Aretino, Benedetto di Bindo was a major source of inspiration for Martino di Bartolomeo's artistic activity after his return to Siena in 1405. But despite Martino's obvious borrowings from the aforementioned artists he always remained a painter with his own personal identity and with a particular affinity to sculpture. This is evident in the central panel of the Falzano altarpiece with the *Assumption of the Virgin*. The painting can be seen as a clear reference to Taddeo di Bartolo's celebrated depiction of the same theme on the central panel of his large altarpiece on the high altar of the cathedral in Montepulciano (1401), yet our artist refrained from bluntly copying Taddeo's interpretation. On the contrary, he gave it fresh vitality by having the Virgin appear in a *mandorla*, akin to a painted sculpture of infinite elegance and of the highest physical and spiritual presence. Undoubtedly the altarpiece from Falzano and with it our *Saint John the Baptist* can be considered one of Martino di Bartolomeo's finest accomplishments and, given the artist's evident interest in Benedetto di Bindos's works painted around 1409-1412, noticeable here, we have good reason to believe that it was probably painted in the course of the second decade of the 15th century, around 1415.

Gaudenz Freuler

3. Martino di Bartolomeo
Maestà (detail)
Siena, Università degli Studi

1) B. Berenson, *Italian Pictures of the Renaissance. Central Italian and North Italian Schools*, London/New York 1968, I, p. 247, pl. 436.
2) L. Speranza, in *Il Museo Diocesano di Cortona*, ed. A. M. Maetzke, Florence 1992, pp. 54-55 (with earlier literature).
3) For this particular aspect of Martino di Bartolomeo's activ-

ity as a painter see *Scultura Dipinta. Maestri di Legname e Pittori a Siena 1250-1450,* exh. cat. (Siena, Pinacoteca Nazionale, 16.7.-31.12.1987), Florence 1987, p. 197, and for a discussion of some of the sculptures painted by him the catalogue entries 27, 37, 40 on pp. 116-118, 148-149, 156-157.

Bibliography:

B. Berenson, *Italian Pictures of the Renaissance. Central Italian and North Italian Schools*, London/New York 1968, I, p. 247, pl. 434
G. Freuler, in *Colnaghi. Master Paintings 1400-1850*, cat. London 1991-1992, London 1991, pp. 12-15.

Zanino di Pietro (Giovanni di Pietro Charlier)

documented from 1389 to 1448

15. Saint Matthew

Tempera on panel, 69 x 23 cm (27 $\frac{1}{6}$ x 9 in.)

Provenance:
Private collection

The panel is in a good state of preservation and has been attributed by Miklós Boskovits to the painter Giovanni Charlier, better known as Zanino di Pietro, and even as Giovanni di Francia.

The painting represents Matthew the Evangelist, depicted with a white beard and hair, standing on a rich marble floor in the act of reading his gospel, embellished on the leather cover by gilded *rote*. The indication of the subject contained in the frame, evidently of a more recent period, seems to preserve a trace of the original *titulus*, possibly marked on the original carpentry and transcribed when the polyptych it belonged to was dismembered. That it is actually Mattew, and not for example John the Evangelist, he also often represented according to Oriental tradition with white hair and beard, can in fact be established with some degree of certainty. Although true that in Venetian circles Matthew was often represented with a short black beard,[1] this characteristic would not appear to be binding. In the polyptych of the Holy Cross from the Augustinian church of San Giacomo Maggiore in Bologna, for example, Paolo Veneziano uses the same features of the beard and white hair and even the same colours of the clothes (the blue of the tunic and the red of the mantle) for both John and Matthew, giving to the former however a noticeably receding hairline and to the latter a much thicker head of hair.

Identifying the figure as Matthew also leads us to hypothesize that the central compartment of the polyptych containing this image represented the Crucifixion, an episode amply described in his gospel (Mat 27:33-61). It is no coincidence in fact that Matthew is represented in the polyptych of San Giacomo in Bologna, in the centre of which was a 'stauroteca' with the relic of the Cross; a position of similar importance is occupied by the same saint in the altar screen by Paolo Veneziano from the church of San Giovanni at Rab, today in the cathedral museum, where it is placed next to the Crucifixion of the main compartment.

The small size of the panel under examination suggests that the original complex comprised two registers, the second of which was presumably occupied by half-figure saints. Its measurements do in fact almost coincide with those (65 x 21 cm) of the compartments of the main register of the polyptych by Lorenzo Veneziano which came from the oratory of the Trinità at the parish church of Santa Maria in Arquà Petrarca, or with those (70 x 21 cm) of the polyptych by the Master of Sant'Elsino today in the Pinacoteca Comunale di Fermo. In the only two polyptychs with a single register known to date as being by Zanino di Pietro, that of the Petit Palais in Avignon and the other from the convent of the Beato Sante at Mombaroccio, the side compartments are instead of a larger size.

At present it is impossible to link any other element to the polyptych from which the panel

under examination comes. Stylistically close, though of a more considerable size (103 x 38 cm) are both the compartment with Saint Peter of the Pinacoteca Comunale di Gubbio (Fig. 1) and the three compartments of the cathedral of Cingoli, though coming from Valcarecce, with the saints Nicholas, Andrew and Lucy, which Federico Zeri[2] has related to the *Madonna and Child* no. 63 of the Pinacoteca Nazionale di Ferrara.

As for the central compartment, if it really contained a Crucifixion, as I believe, it cannot be the panel with that subject formerly in the Chillingworth collection in Lucerne,[3] formerly in the centre of a polyptych that has been hypothesized as similar to that of Mombaroccio,[4] nor can it be the one of the City Museum in Split, of which it has been impossible to take measurements although it does not seem to belong to a large complex.

1. Zanino di Pietro
Saint Peter
Gubbio, Pinacoteca Comunale

118

2. Zanino di Pietro
Virgin and Child
Rome, Museo di Palazzo Venezia

The painting under examination represents an important addition to the list of works by Giovanni di Pietro Charlier, which has been augmented most recently, following a suggestion by Zeri taken up by Serena Padovani,[5] also by the works that critics have grouped around the *Virgin and Child* (Fig. 2) signed by "Johannes de Francia" and dated 1429 (Rome, Museo di Palazzo Venezia). This has given substance to the biography of a French painter with Venetian citizenship, who between 1389 and 1406 was documented at Bologna[6] and from 1407 was again in Venice, where presumably he would remain until his death some time before 1448.[7] The works that critics previously attributed to Zanino, a diminutive form of Giovanni, grouping them around the triptych of the Franciscan convent of Fonte Colombo (Rieti, Museo Civico), signed "Zanin[us] Petri habitator Venexiis in contrata Sancte Apollinaris", correspond roughly to the painter's early activity, while those grouped under the name of Giovanni di Francia seem to belong to his latter years.

3. Zanino di Pietro
Madonna of Humility
Private collection

Mention has already been made of how much the painter, in the course of his early artistic activity, owed to the Bolognese figurative school, particularly the neo-Giottism of Jacopo di Paolo and the use of colour of the illuminator Nicolò di Giacomo, evident for example in the *Madonna of Humility* (Fig. 3) in a private collection[8] or in the afore-mentioned polyptych of the Musée du Petit Palais in Avignon (inv. M. I. 421). Subsequently his style was influenced above all by that of Gentile da Fabriano, who was certainly present in Venice some years before 1408, when he was documented there. Despite the still solid construction and the frowning expression, harking back to his Bolognese experience, the *Saint Matthew* under examination now follows this new model, as is shown by the lazy replication of the drapery, with the hems accentuated in pastiglia and further embellished by a play of punchmarks, the no less precious working of the halo, comparable with that of the *Saint Peter* in the Pinacoteca Comunale di Gubbio, and the subtle highlights on the flowing mass of hair and beard, executed *currenti penicillo* according to the mellow, sumptuous taste imposed in Venice by Gentile da Fabriano.

4. Zanino di Pietro
Annunciation (detail)
Venice, Santa Maria Gloriosa dei Frari

The face of Matthew finds in the humanity of the painter more than one comparison, though particularly stringent is the one with God the Father of the *Annunciation* (Fig. 4) embellishing the tomb monument of the Beato Pacifico in the basilica dei Frari in Venice, executed before 1436 to house the mortal remains of the procurator of the building of the basilica Scipione Bon. Zanino di Pietro appears at this time to be fully aware also of the results achieved by other artists in Venice who were developing the ideas of Gentile da Fabriano, from Jacobello del Fiore to Michele Giambono: and it is in particular the opulent and decadent taste of the latter that is reflected in the painting under examination, confirming a date of execution fairly late on in the final years of the painter's artistic activity. This constant ability to keep up to date with new influences played a significant role in Zanino's popularity with varied and geographically widespread patrons between Veneto and the Marches.

Fabio Massaccesi

1) G. Kaftal, *Iconography of the Saints in the Painting of North East Italy*, Florence 1978, col. 729.

2) In A. Bacchi, in *Il Tempo di Nicolò III. Gli affreschi del castello di Vignola e la pittura tardogotica nei domini estensi*, exh. cat. (Vignola), ed. D. Benati, Modena 1988, pp. 143-144 no. 19.

3) F. Zeri, *Aggiunte a Zanino di Pietro*, 'Paragone', 153, 1962, pp. 56-60.

4) A. De Marchi, in *Pittura Veneta nelle Marche*, ed. V. Curzi, 2000, p. 84 n. 125.

5) S. Padovani, *Una nuova proposta per Zanino di Pietro*, 'Paragone', 419-421-423, 1985, pp. 71-79.

6) F. Filippini, G. Zucchini, *Miniatori e pittori a Bologna. Documenti dei secoli XIII e XIV*, Florence 1947, pp. 239-240.

7) P. Paoletti, *La Ca' d'Oro in Venezia*, I, 1920, p. 120 n. 2.

8) S. Padovani, *Una nuova proposta per Zanino* cit., fig. 58.

Giovanni di Paolo

Siena, 1398-1482

16. The Virgin and Child between Saints Catherine of Alexandria, Dorothy (?) and two Angels

Tempera on panel 34.6 x 22.6 cm (13 ⁵/₈ x 8 ⁷/₈ in.)

Provenance:
London, private collection
Paris, Giovanni Sarti Gallery

The panel is extremely slim (9 mm), yet it appears original and not thinned, which is atypical for this kind of artifact. A crack runs down it vertically, passing through the proper left eye of the Child, though despite this the gold and the other faces are in a remarkably good condition. The panel has been slightly cropped at the bottom, where the saints' feet are no longer visible, and especially at the top, where the original gable, its distinctive vertical form characteristic of Siena in the late Gothic period, has been reduced to a trapezoidal shape. Conservation treatment has built up the pointed outline, with the restored parts visible, so that the work can once again have the pristine elegance of a slender pinnacle (though the sharp angle of the gable rules out the former presence of any other image, such as a figure of God the Father).[1] It is likely that this was the central panel of a small portable tabernacle with folding shutters, the kind of object created by Giovanni di Paolo on many occasions, highly refined in quality and with wings that were often very tall and narrow.[2] The female saint on the left, crowned and holding a martyr's palm, could only be Saint Catherine of Alexandria (numerous Sienese paintings present her without her typical attribute, the spiked wheel), while the crowned saint on the right, holding white and red roses in the waist-high fold of her cloak, should be Saint Dorothy.[3] The Child, his legs crossed as he is held up by his mother in a solemn pose – inherited from that of the 13th-century Madonna Hodegetria type – blesses with his right hand and holds a scroll in his left with the inscription "[e]GO SVM VIA VERIT[as et vita]".

The problem of attribution here is not a simple one. I believe that Laurence Kanter hit the mark when he suggested it was a very early work by Giovanni di Paolo – a hypothesis agreed upon by Everett Fahy. The painting's conscious and remarkable revival of great Sienese art of the early 14th century, and particularly that of Simone Martini's maturity, could easily lead one astray. The attenuated, highly elegant silhouette of the Madonna, moving her shoulders gently away from the vertical axis, and frontally inclining her head in a melancholy way, is explicitly Simonesque, and seems to imply an awareness of his innermost circle during his later years of such works as the *Virgin and Child with four Archangels* by the Master of the Palazzo Venezia Madonna (Fig. 1), in the Berenson collection at Villa I Tatti, which is recalled here in a fairly evident manner. In the altarpiece, the curved space around the front of the Virgin's throne is beautifully defined solely by incising the gold surface of the drapery held open by two flying angels. In the painting before us, on the other hand, there is no complex structural reference to the throne, which is defined simply by the planes of red and orange cloth, differentiated according to whether they are shaded or lit; the cloth itself flows uninterruptedly across the dais (its raised part visible), over the throne

1. Master of the Palazzo Venezia Madonna
Virgin and Child with four Archangels
Florence, Villa I Tatti

2. Giovanni di Paolo (attr.)
Virgin and Child with Saint John the Baptist,
Saint John the Evangelist and two Angels
Tours, Musée des Beaux-Arts

itself and on the simple seat, foreshortened along its receding sides. It is clear that this painter was fascinated by the underlying gold leaf – present in most of the dresses – and he exploited it by applying translucent glazes and scratching through them with minute incisions. The so-called 'sgraffito' technique, perfected by Simone Martini and Lippo Memmi in the *Annunciation* triptych painted in 1333 for the altar of Saint Ansanus in Siena cathedral, is adopted here using the finest tooling – apparently solely with pointed *granitura*, or granulated series of dots, though in fact created by punching tiny circles – on the sky-blue tunic of Saint Catherine and on the verdigris robes, now aged into a brownish hue,[4] of the two angels. Other materials, such as the Virgin's robe (also painted over gold), or the outer side of the angels' cloaks, glazed in yellow, are enlivened by swift, tiny strokes made with the point of a stylus, similar to the definition of the wing feathers, revealing gold under the pigment; while the sumptuous linings of the cloaks worn by Saint Dorothy and the angel on the right carefully imitate the checkered lining of the Archangel Gabriel's cloak in the *Annunciation* of 1333 – a prototype that was incessantly admired and imitated by later Sienese painters, even in precise copies made by Bartolo di Fredi and Matteo di Giovanni. In the painting by Simone Martini and Lippo Memmi the textile squares are worked with lightly incised tendrils, and the inner parts of the orthogonals with sgraffito incision of braid motifs; here the motif is emulated on a minimal scale, and the painter does not fail to incise the inner lines of the orthogonals. The miniature dimensions probably led the painter to abstain from the usual decorations in mordant gold along the hem of the Virgin's blue cloak, now darkened (as is typically the case) and thus with its indented modulation flattened; the pearl border of this hem is created in white, with the tip of the paintbrush. How the artist competed, generations later, with the great standard set by Simone is also implicit in the special quality of the tooling. The decoration along the inner side of the border in the background is particularly noteworthy: instead of the usual small arches, the artist uses a tiny lobed punchmark, spreading into two symmetrically facing tendril motifs and enclosing a triangle.[5] Even the illusionistic jewelry in their crowns, described with the smallest of punchmarks, with drops of lead white to suggest pearls, and red and blue for other precious stones, is based on models found in Simone Martini.

The miraculously virtuoso quality of these pictorial techniques is combined with a markedly linear figure style involving incisive description of eyebrows, facial features, undulating hair falling in regular curls, and hands with thread-like fingers. The saints and two angels have attenuated, quite lean bodies, with elbows bent in acute angles, and the Virgin's cloak falls to the ground in broken rather than sweetly sinuous lines. This nervous, linear quality is characteristic of all of Giovanni di Paolo's work, even though this is of course not such a typical work; if, as I believe, it is in fact by him, then it should be dated to a very early and still substantially unexplored period of his career. There is no trace yet of the influence of Gentile da Fabriano, who sojourned in Siena in 1424-1425, and whose style was to felicitously graft itself onto the already marked penchant for goldsmiths' techniques of the early Trecento, and especially for the art of Simone Martini. Laurence Kanter has suggested connecting this little panel with four fragments from the wings of a similar triptych – the *Saint James the Greater* in the F. Mason Perkins collection in the Sacro Convento di San Francesco, Assisi, the *Archangel Gabriel* in the Musée du Petit Palais, Avignon, a *Saint Christopher* formerly in the Moratilla collection, and an *Annunciate Virgin* in a private collection in New York.[6] These fragments should however be understood alongside the panels of the Malavolti-Pecci polyptych of 1426, and are more typical, unmistakable works by Giovanni di Paolo; moreover, the angle of the gable, which can be deduced from the tooled border of the Archangel Gabriel in Avignon, was less acute, and the border itself appears to be different.[7] A reconstruction of Giovanni di Paolo's initial period is still an open question. We now know that he was born in 1398[8] and was first documented as an independent master on 5 September 1417, when he painted miniatures in a book of hours destined for Anna, the wife of the Lombard jurist Cristoforo Castiglioni, a cousin of the famous Cardinal Branda di Castiglione, and paid for by the Dominican friar Niccolò Galgani.[9] In 1419 Giovanni painted an image of Catherine of Siena (still Blessed, before she became a saint) for the nuns of Santa Marta. Yet what his painting looked like in these earliest years is still rather mysterious. The painter's first dated work is a cylindrical wedding box in the Louvre (inv. OA 2517) with a *Triumph of Venus* on the cover, dated 1421 and recognized by Millard Meiss as his first work;[10] this was before the polyptych of 1426 formerly in San Domenico on the Pecci altar, but earlier apparently on the Malavolti altar, an ensemble now divided between Castelnuovo Berardenga (Fig. 4), the Pinacoteca Nazionale in Siena, the Lindenau-Museum, Altenburg, and the Walters Art Gallery, Baltimore, and which provides us with the most commonly accepted start to his career.[11] Bearing in mind the secular subject (hunting dogs chasing deer and boars) painted on the sides of the wedding box in the Louvre, and the origins of his first patron, scholars have often spoken of Lombard influences on Giovanni di Paolo's initial development, yet this is nowhere supported by style. It has also been hypothesized that he was apprenticed to Taddeo di Bartolo, by whom one work (the *Virgin and Child with two Angels* in the central part of the triptych painted for the Compagnia di Santa Caterina della

3. Giovanni di Paolo
The Virgin and Child between Saints Catherine of Alexandria,
Dorothy (?) and two Angels (detail)
Cat. 16

4. Giovanni di Paolo
Virgin and Child with Angels (detail)
Castelnuovo Berardenga (Siena), church of
San Giusto e Clemente

Notte, signed and dated 1400) was copied in the central composition of the Malavolti-Pecci polyptych. Throughout his life, Giovanni di Paolo drew widely from the most disparate sources, combining them with bizarre imagination, and thus even this obvious deduction cannot offer secure evidence for his initial training. The echo of Simone Martini in the painting presented here is in line with the rediscovery of the great master that was already being carried out by protagonists of late Trecento painting such as Francesco di Vannuccio, and, in part, Paolo di Giovanni Fei – names often invoked to explain Giovanni di Paolo's beginnings. The markedly graphic aspect that defines the forms reminds one of painters like Bartolo di Fredi and Francesco di Vannuccio, but also of those who were chronologically closer to the young Giovanni di Paolo, and whom he could have known, like Benedetto di Bindo and Martino di Bartolomeo. During the 1410s, while establishing himself in a fairly prestigious way in Siena, where he had returned from Pisa in 1405, Martino himself developed an explicit revival of Simone Martini, also as regards technique, reflected for example in a beautiful *Risen Christ* in the church of San Clemente at Sociana in the upper Valdarno,[12] which dates from these years, when he was at his best. In the mid-1410s, then, it is not impossible that Giovanni di Paolo emerged alongside Martino di Bartolomeo, and an appropriate clue is provided by the fact that in later years, around 1430, the two artists collaborated in an entirely formal way, as proved by a predella comprising a series of saints depicted in tondi – divided between the Johnson collection in Philadelphia Museum of Art (*Saint Lawrence* and *A Deacon Saint* by Giovanni di Paolo) and the York City Art Gallery (*Saint Peter* and *Saint Paul* by Martino di Bartolomeo) – that involved both painters; the work was reassembled by Federico Zeri.[13] While it is qualitatively on a higher level than the work of Martino di Bartolomeo, our panel might support this hypothesis, and using it as a benchmark may enable us to start to fill in this still obscure period of Giovanni di Paolo's career. We may thus consider a small panel in the Musée des Beaux-Arts in Tours (inv. 63.2.7) with the *Virgin and Child between Saints John the Baptist, John the Evangelist, two Angels and God the Father* (Fig. 2), which survives in a slightly problematic state, and which presents not only a similar return to the models established by Simone Martini and Lippo Memmi – as indicated by Michel Laclotte, who attributed the work to an anonymous artist of the second half of the 14th century[14] – but a similar predilection for straight, incisive lines, as well as some remarkably refined details in the minute, prehensile articulation of the hands of the Virgin and Child.

Andrea De Marchi

1) As is visible, for instance, at the top of the central panel of a triptych by Giovanni di Paolo, datable to about 1430, formerly with Patrick Matthiesen in London and now in the Los Angeles County Museum of Art (see F. Dabell, in *Matthiesen Fine Art Ltd. Gold Backs 1250-1480*, London 1996, pp. 111-117).

2) Examples include the reassembled triptych in the Kimbell Art Museum, Forth Worth (H. W. Van Os, *Reassembling a Giovanni di Paolo Triptych*, 'The Burlington Magazine', CXIX, 1977, pp. 191-192) and the one in the Pinacoteca Nazionale, Siena (inv. 179: see P. Torriti, *La Pinacoteca Nazionale di Siena*, Genoa 1990, pp. 221-222), a fairly late work, where the painter adopts Simone's motif of the Virgin and Child, the latter frontal, blessing, and holding a scroll.

3) Victor Schmidt has recently presented convincing arguments that many of the presumed depictions of Saint Dorothy in Sienese art, starting with that in Ambrogio Lorenzetti's polyptych in the Pinacoteca Nazionale, Siena (from the convent of Santa Petronilla), should instead be recognized as of Saint Martha (V. M. Schmidt, *La Santa con i fiori. Sul polittico di Ambrogio Lorenzetti dalla chiesa di Santa Petronilla*, 'Prospettiva', 119-120, 2005, pp. 88-94). However, this does not appear to be the case in our painting, where the floral crown should be a reference to the glory of martyrdom; Saint Martha was not a martyr.

4) Verdigris is also the color of the fictive marble flooring, which we must imagine as a brilliant green rather than the current brown. The same pigment was also used in the lining of Saint Dorothy's cloak, and on her robe.

5) There is still a need for a census of the punchmarks used by Sienese painters of the early Quattrocento, comparable to the studies regarding Tuscan painting of the Trecento made by Erling Skaug and Mojmír Frinta. A careful analysis of this particular punchmark within the oeuvre of Giovanni di Paolo and other painters of his time, which I was unable to do on this occasion, would furnish valuable evidence for further study.

6) For the reconstruction of these two wings, begun by Federico Zeri and perfected by Kanter with the addition of the *Annunciate Virgin* (London, Sotheby's sale, 26 April 2004, lot 18), see the photomontage in M. Laclotte and E. Moench, *Peinture italienne. Musée du Petit Palais Avignon*, Paris 2005, pp. 110, 236, no. 101.

7) This presents a series of small three-lobed arches joined in a highly distinctive way, indicative of the experimental technique of the young Giovanni di Paolo, with foliate punchmarks.

8) In fact Wolfgang Loseries has identified the baptismal record of 28 June 1398 (see D. Sallay, *Giovanni di Paolo*, in *Allgemeines Künstlerlexicon. Die bildenden Künstler aller Zeiten und Völker*, LV, Munich-Leipzig 2007, p. 55). In the past an erroneous connection had been made with another Giovanni di Paolo who was baptized in Siena on 19 November 1403.

9) See C. B. Strehlke, in *Painting in Renaissance Siena 1420-1500*, exh. cat. (New York), eds. K. Christiansen, L. B. Kanter and C. B. Strehlke, New York 1988, p. 168; D. Sallay, *Giovanni di Paolo* cit., p. 55.

10) M. Meiss, *The Earliest Work of Giovanni di Paolo*, 'Art in America', XXIV, 1936, 4, pp. 137-143; G. Chelazzi Dini, in *Il gotico a Siena. Miniature pitture oreficerie oggetti d'arte*, exh. cat. (Siena), Florence 1982, p. 359, no. 128; *eadem*, in *L'art gothique siennois. Enluminure, peinture, orfèvrerie, sculpture*, exh. cat. (Avignon), Florence 1983, pp. 318-319, no. 114.

11) See I. Bähr, *Die Altarretabel des Giovanni di Paolo aus San Domenico in Siena. Überlegungen zu den Auftraggebern*, 'Mitteilungen des Kunsthistorischen Institutes', XXXI, 1987, pp. 357-366; and A. Labriola, in *Maestri senesi e toscani nel Lindenau-Museum di Altenburg*, exh. cat. (Siena), ed. M. Boskovits, Siena 2008, pp. 146-151.

12) The painting – recently restored under the supervision of Caterina Caneva, to whom I am grateful for her availability – was formerly ascribed to Paolo di Giovanni Fei by Luciano Bellosi (see A. Conti, *Dipinti e committenti nel piviere di Rignano*, in A. Conti, I. Moretti and M. Barducci, *Rignano sull'Arno. Tre studi sul patrimonio culturale*, Florence 1986, pp. 61, 65) and is now illustrated by Gabriele Fattorini as a work by Martino di Bartolomeo in an article that makes a structured analysis of the painter's entire mature period (G. Fattorini, *La pala dei Carnaioli per Sant'Antonio Abate in Fontebranda a Siena: l'ultima opera documentata di Martino di Bartolomeo e Francesco di Valdambrino*, in the issue of 'Nuovi studi. Rivista di arte antica e moderna', XII, 2007, 13).

13) F. Zeri, *Diari di lavoro 3. Giovanni di Paolo e Martino di Bartolomeo: una proposta*, 'Paragone', XXXVII, 1986, 435, pp. 6-7; C. B. Strehlke, *Italian Paintings 1250-1450 in the John G. Johnson Collection and the Philadelphia Museum of Art*, Philadelphia 2004, pp. 174-176.

14) M. Laclotte, in *L'art gothique siennois* cit., p. 260, no. 97. The rectangular painting has a separate triangular gable and measures 44 x 22 cm.

Bibliography:

A. De Marchi, *Giovanni di Paolo*, in *Da Jacopo della Quercia a Donatello*, exh. cat. (Siena, Santa Maria della Scala, 26.3.-11.7.2010) under the direction of M. Seidel, Milan 2010, pp. 198-199, no. 8

Auf Goldenem Grund, exh. cat. (Vienna, Liechtenstein Museum, 12.12.2008-14.4.2009) under the direction of J. Kräftner, Vienna 2008, pp. 54-55, no. 25.

ANSANO DI ANDREA DI BARTOLO (?)

Siena, 1421-1491

17. Virgin and Child

Tempera on panel, 57 x 48 cm (22 $^2/_5$ x 18 $^7/_8$ in.)

Provenance:
Private collection

The exquisite little panel with the *Virgin and Child*, presented here, is one of the most intriguing recent rediscoveries of Sienese Quattrocento painting. The image is a retrospective, early Renaissance interpretation of a type invented and established by the greatest Sienese painters from as early as the first half of the 14th century in a form that has come down to us in Simone Martini's *Madonna and Child* in the Wallraf-Richartz-Museum in Cologne (no. 880) (Fig. 1).

The Virgin holds her Son with tender affection and gently bows her head towards him. He seems not to respond to his mother's graceful attentions, appearing instead to be wrapt in profound contemplation – perhaps about his mission as the Saviour that would bring him pain and suffering on the Cross, an event which is alluded to by the goldfinch trapped in the little red shoe which he holds in his left hand. The generally composed atmosphere of the scene is animated by the lively cherubim and seraphim which, with their lively rounded faces, more than recalling angels close to God, remind us of loud rascals.

If we now investigate the artist who painted this beautiful Madonna, we are inevitably confronted with the artistic situation in Siena that gravitated around the young Vecchietta.

After a brief spell in the late 1430s in Castiglione Olona (near Milan), as an assistant in Masolino's workshop, he returned to Siena, where in the 1440s he quickly established himself as one of the most progressive artists in the city. This was a time when the Renaissance avant-garde of Sienese painters, headed by Domenico di Bartolo and Lorenzo Vecchietta, were eagerly assimilating the innovations of the leading Florentine artists of the early Renaissance. Following in the footsteps of the leading Florentine painters and sculptors – Masaccio, Masolino, Filippo Lippi, Lorenzo Ghiberti and Donatello – they reformed the traditional formulas of Sienese painting without breaking with their own well-established traditions. As is also the case with our *Madonna*, these artists permeated their old Sienese formulas and inventions with a Renaissance spirit and produced pictures of major physical substance, consequently scenes of higher empathy, and, in the case of the splendid frescoes of the Pellegrinaio of the Ospedale di Santa Maria della Scala in Siena, episodes embedded in fantastic architectural settings, constructed as eccentric expressions of the newly acquired rules of perspective within an artistic vocabulary of no lesser eccentricity inspired by the classical world.

Although certain stylistic formulas and abstractions of the present *Madonna* are linked to the style of Vecchietta's painting, which suggest they were conceived in a workshop close to this painter, it is also true that the painting, despite its innovative Renaissance feel, essentially has a retrospective, distinctly linear quality which is in contrast to Vecchietta's innovations.

1. Simone Martini
Virgin and Child
Cologne, Wallraf-Richartz Museum

Emphasizing the linear and ornamental touches, like the extensive use of 'sgraffito' for the angel's wings, making them look as if they are covered in a splendorous glittering spider's web, the unknown painter eschews the sculptural solidity that characterized the figures of Vecchietta's paintings. The wonderfully modelled faces of the Virgin and her Child are rendered with exquisitely modelled flesh-tones which, thanks to the delicate nuances of light and shade, take on an enamel-like quality. It is precisely this aspect that reminds us of the later works of the Master of the Osservanza (young Sano di Pietro), such as for example the splendid kneeling figure of Saint Ansanus, formerly with De Carlo in Florence and later with Moretti in Prato (Fig. 2),[1] datable towards the end of the fourth decade of the 14th century, or the triptych with the *Assumption of the Virgin* from the chapel of the Befa di Monteapertuso near Murlo (Siena), now in the Pinacoteca Nazionale di Siena (no. 15), a work that is half-way between Vecchietta and the dry harshness of Pietro di Giovanni Ambrosi.[2] The preciousness of the garments with large ornaments as seen in the above-mentioned paintings is a clear reference to Gentile da Fabriano, whose activity in Siena and Florence, as early as 1426 (Giovanni di Paolo's from San Domenico),[3] left a long-lasting impact on Sienese Quat-

trocento painters. This careful attention to the ornamental embellishment of the pictorial surface – be it the angel's wings with their double interplay of 'sgraffito' in the double silver- and gold-ground, be it the garments of the Virgin or the superbly worked silver ground of the Child's mantle – represents a remarkable technical achievement and has the quality of a monumental goldsmith's work. The splendid filigree pattern incised into the double silver and gold-ground, producing at the same time a wonderful interplay of gold, silver and brilliant red, gives the painting an incredibly ethereal effect, turning the picture into a heavenly vision of divine actors which nevertheless have maintained their human nature.

All the artistic qualities mentioned here raise the question of who painted this brilliant little panel.

The answer to this question can only be of a hypothetical nature. However, our observations regarding this painting, particularly the link with Vecchietta's art and Sienese painting generally between 1430 and 1450, suggest that he should be sought among those painters who had assisted Vecchietta during his early period, when in 1440 he was commissioned to execute the frescoes in the Ospedale di Santa Maria della Scala in Siena. In this fertile ground, where he was able to give free expression to his great artistic talent, in 1445/46 Vecchietta's

2. Maestro dell'Osservanza (Sano di Pietro)
Saint Ansanus
Florence, Carlo De Carlo collection (formerly)
Prato, Moretti collection (formerly)

3. Bartolo di Fredi
Angel (detail)
Private collection

workshop was involved in producing and painting the *Arliquiera* (reliquary cabinet). The documents relating to this project are particularly significant with respect to our artist insofar as they mention two of the artistic inspirers of our painter mentioned above, the head of the project, Vecchietta, and the Sienese painter Giovanni di Pietro Ambrosi. In addition to these artists we hear of a third collaborator, a painter without oeuvre and still awaiting to be identified, therefore Ansano di Andrea di Bartolo (1421-1491), the last offspring of a long painter's dynasty.[4] Ansano was the last descendant of his grandfather Bartolo di Fredi (ca. 1330-1410) and the son of Andrea di Bartolo (ca. 1365-1429). His documented assistance in Vecchietta's *Arliquiera* project has long been debated, and various attempts have been made to identify the nature of Ansano's contribution within this artistic effort. But no conclusive consensus has been reached as regards the division of work within the production of this splendid object.[5]

The crux in the difficult task of distinguishing the hands that worked on this piece might be that Vecchietta may have demanded of his assistants a complete assimilation of his style and that he may at the same time have delegated to them the most humble and specialized tasks, such as the tooling of the gold ground and other minor responsibilities.

Interestingly enough, it is precisely the precious tooling of the gold ground of the various Sienese saints and blesseds in the *Arliquiera* that reveals an execution similar to the decoration of the garments of the protagonists in our little panel.

In this context it might be worth mentioning that Ansano di Andrea di Bartolo, apart from being documented as a painter and miniaturist (companion to Sano di Pietro), is also referred to as a craftsman specialized in the chasing of gold.[6] With regard to Vecchietta's other assistant cited in the document, the well-known Pietro di Giovanni Ambrosi, it is certain that his characteristically brittle and angular style, even though assimilated with that of Vecchietta, emerged in various scenes of the Passion (e.g. in the *Crucifixion* itself). It is also

4. Andrea di Bartolo
Madonna of Humility
Asciano (Siena), Salini collection

true, however, that in other scenes of the Passion cycle (e.g. the *Ascent to Calvary* and the *Capture of Christ*) we find smooth and softly modelled enamel-like faces which compare in texture with what we see in the Virgin under discussion.

The collaboration on Vecchietta's *Arliquiera* might be summarized in the following terms: Vecchietta probably designed the whole concept of the *Arliquiera* and executed the magnificent series of Sienese saints and blesseds. The execution of the small scenes, even though they too were conceived by the master himself, may have been delegated to his two assistants. Finally, the highly specialized task of tooling the gold ground may have been left to a skilled craftsman in this field, the documented Ansano di Andrea di Bartolo, who as we have already mentioned was an expert gold-beater.

If the talented unknown artist from Vecchietta's artistic entourage who painted the present *Madonna* was indeed the documented Ansano di Andrea di Bartolo, we may also have found a plausible answer for the expertise and the great attention given to the working of the gold and silver ground. Interestingly enough, the rare feature of a double silver and gold ground seems to be a usage that is also traceable in the oeuvre of Ansano's grandfather Bartolo di

Fredi, who chose this technique in his altarpiece for the Compagnia di San Pietro Martire in the Sienese church of San Domenico.[7] This particular technique, therefore, may have been passed on within the family from generation to generation.

Another significant clue is afforded by the painter's apparent familiarity with the art, inventions and typological formulas of the previous century, since they were probably handed down by his forebears, Bartolo di Fredi and Andrea di Bartolo. All this fits in well with a painter like Ansano di Andrea di Bartolo, who was born into a long-established artistic family, which for many decades was committed to perpetuating the formulas of its founder Bartolo di Fredi. It hardly comes as a surprise, therefore, if in a painting such as the present *Madonna*, which otherwise clearly observes the aesthetic and artistic canons of the Renaissance, we encounter a retrospective return to archaic figural types like the angels with chubby faces (Fig. 3) which, in spite of their firm articulation, clearly perpetuate their prototypes created more than half a century earlier by Bartolo di Fredi, like the seraph in the pinnacle with the *Blessing Christ* in a private collection. Even the frontal face of the Christ Child, although rendered with a more modern enamelled chiaroscuro modelling, seems, with its stylized curls, a more evolved derivation from older models which had been similarly created by Ansano's father Andrea di Bartolo, e.g. his Child in a Madonna of Humility in the Salini collection near Asciano (Fig. 4) which dates from Andrea's final phase in Venice.[8]

The style of our *Madonna*, datable to the fifth decade of the 15th century and firmly rooted in Vecchietta's art, soon after his return from Castiglione Olona, as well as several other aspects that conform with the biography of the shadowy Ansano di Andrea di Bartolo – especially his role as Vecchietta's assistant on the *Arliquiera* project and his expertise in the working of the gold- and silver ground – have prompted us, with all the necessary caution, to assign this charming painting to Ansano di Andrea di Bartolo, a painter, miniaturist and expert in the working of gold.

Gaudenz Freuler

1) A. De Marchi, in *Da Jacopo della Quercia a Donatello. Le Arti a Siena nel primo Rinascimento*, exh. cat. (Siena, 26.3.-11.7.2010), Siena 2010, pp. 272-275.

2) P. Torriti, *La Pinacoteca Nazionale di Siena*, Genoa 1990, pp. 258-259.

3) D. Sallay, in *Da Jacopo della Quercia a Donatello* cit., pp. 206-209.

4) For the archival documents, cf. P. Bacci, *Documenti e commenti per la storia dell'arte*, Florence 1944, pp. 105-106.

5) H. W. van Os, *Vecchietta and the Sacristy of the Siena Hospital Church*, The Hague 1974, p. 16 ff; P. Torriti, *La Pinacoteca* cit., pp. 259-253; D. Gallavotti Cavallero, *Lo Spedale di Santa Maria della Scala in Siena*, Siena 1985, p. 173 ff.

6) For the biographical data of Ansano di Andrea di Bartolo, cf. E. Romagnoli, *Biografia cronologica de' Bellartisti senesi dal secolo XII a tutto il XVIII*, ca. 1835 (ed. Florence 1976), IV, pp. 495-502; V. Lusini, *Il Duomo di Siena, II*, Siena 1939, *passim*. For a recent discussion of Ansano di Andrea di Bartolo's

activity as a beater of gold, cf. W. Loseries, *Bartolo di Fredi riabilitato*, 'La Diana', II, 1996, pp. 463-464, who rightly (and in contrast to my previous opinion) recognizes an identity of Ansano di Andrea di Bartolo the painter and Ansano di Bartolo the gold-beater (i.e. a craftsman responsible for preparing gold leaf).

7) This double silver and gold ground is visible in the much damaged *Madonna* ex-Briganti which has recently resurfaced on the Milanese art market (Milan, Christie's, Old Masters Painting, 25.11.2011, lot. 41) and the panel above with the *Assumption of the Virgin*, formerly in Cap Ferrat and now as a deposit in the Musée Marmottan in Paris; G. Freuler, *Bartolo di Fredi Cini, Ein Beitrag zur sienesischen Malerei des 14. Jahrhunderts*, Disentis 1994, pp. 124-133, 449-452.

8) G. Freuler, in *La Collezione Salini. Dipinti, sculture e oreficerie dei secoli XII, XIII, XIV e XV*, ed. L. Bellosi, I, Florence 2009, pp. 250-255.

Bibliography:
G. Freuler, in *Pittori attivi in Toscana dal Trecento al Settecento*, ed. F. Baldassari, cat. Galleria Moretti, Florence 2001, pp. 68-77.

MASTER OF THE FIESOLE EPIPHANY
Florence, 1449-1503

18a. Triptych: Stigmata of Saint Francis and the Archangel Gabriel *(left wing)*; Saint Jerome in the Desert and the Virgin Annunciate *(right wing)*; Christ in Pietà between two Franciscan Saints, the Virgin and Saint Barbara *(base tapering towards the bottom)*

Tempera on panel, closed 67 x 32 x 11.5 cm (26 3/8 x 12 1/2 x 4 1/2 in.), open 67 x 64.5 cm (26 3/8 x 25 3/8 in.)

PIETRO AND GIOVANNI ALEMANNO (ATTR.)
active in Campania in the second half of the 15th century

18b. Virgin and Child

Wooden sculpture, height 42.5 cm (16 3/4 in.)

Provenance:
New York, Piero Tozzi
Florence, Carlo De Carlo collection
Florence, Lisa De Carlo collection

This is a small tabernacle certainly destined for private worship, which in the central niche contains a wooden sculpture representing the Virgin and Child. The inner wings contain rich painted representations, with the Angel of the Annunciation on the left and, on the opposite side, the corresponding Virgin Annunciate. Lower down, Saint Francis receiving the stigmata corresponds fontally with the Saint Jerome in penitence. The base is decorated with a Christ in Pietà with two Franciscan saints, the Virgin and Saint Barbara, the latter identifiable by the tower she holds in her hand. This is one of those folding portable altarpieces often mentioned in the inventories of 15th-century residences. Very few houses at the time, even aristocratic ones, possessed private chapels: in the absence of a room set aside for this purpose, prayer and devotion were for the most part carried out in the bedroom.[1] The preacher Dominici (ca. 1410) recommended to all good fathers "d'aver dipinture in casa di santi e fanciulli o vergini giovinette, nelle quali il tuo figliuolo ancor nelle fasce, si diletti come simile e dal simile rapito, con atti e segni grati all'infanzia. E come dico dipinture cosi dico di scolture". And continued, "Bene sta la Vergine Maria col fanciullo in braccio e l'uccellino o la melograna in pugno. Sarà buona figura Iesù che poppa, Iesù che dorma in grembo della madre, Iesù le sta cortese innanzi".[2] In effect, these subjects were the inspiration for roundels, portable tabernacles, with or without closable wings, "colmi da camera" or "tabernacoli centinati" and reliefs in terracotta that covered the walls of the bedroom:[3] treated with veneration and protected by veils and curtains, prayers were made in front of these images by the light of candles.[4] From the literature of the period we know that the Renaissance man had an even physical contact with these objects, kissing them and embracing them, and thus establishing a rapport of intense devotion.[5] As we learn from the *Ricordanze* of Neri di Bicci, painted or sculpted tabernacles might also be destined for the rooms of convents, for the prayers of monks and nuns, a plausible hypothesis for the work in question considering the iconographical reference to Franciscan saints.

The type of decoration seems to follow figurative traditions for this kind of object: in fact, the two wings of the portable altarpiece by Neri di Bicci (Florence, Palazzo Davanzati, inv.

1890, no. 5888) also represent the Virgin Annunciate and the Archangel of the Annunciation in the upper part, and below the figures of Saint Benedict and the Archangel with Tobias. From the point of view of style, both in the typologies and in the background landscapes, we perceive references to Jacopo del Sellaio, although it is impossible here to recognize his hand in the work. As Everett Fahy has mentioned in various publications,[6] we have here a work by the Master of the Fiesole Epiphany, a Florentine painter who gets his conventional name from the *Adoration of the Magi* which came from the Benedictine convent of the Murate in Florence (ca. 1490), though is presently in the church of San Francesco in Fiesole (Florence; Fig. 1).[7] In actual fact the Saint Francis of our small tabernacle shows significant similarities with the same saint of the Fiesole panel, which is linked to the work exhibited here also from the point of view of the jagged rocky landscape of the background. The same descriptive character which characterizes the New York aedicule and the Fiesole panel returns in the *Coronation of the Virgin* of the Accademia (inv. 1890, no. 490; Fig. 2), where the lineaments of the Virgin are superimposed on the Saint Barbara of the base of the tabernacle.

The stylistic characteristics of the anonymous master, influenced on the one hand by the art of Jacopo del Sellaio, on the other by that of Ghirlandaio, although also not insensitive to the works of Cosimo Rosselli, induced Fahy to identify the artist hypothetically as Filippo di Giuliano,[8] documented in 1473 as the "companion", that is the partner, of the above-mentioned Jacopo, with whom it appears he shared a workshop in San Miniato fra le Torri in 1480 and in 1490.[9] This attribution has also been accepted by Padoa Rizzo,[10] even though firm elements to back up this certainly intriguing hypothesis are for the time being lacking. It seems that in 1472 Filippo di Giuliano was not only painting but also making naibi, or playing cards, and appears to be carrying out these two activities in different workshops.[11] In 1483 Filippo di Giuliano is documented as working in Palazzo Vecchio in Florence, in contact with Domenico Ghirlandaio who at the time was frescoing the Sala dei Gigli in the same building.[12] From the end of the 1470s we also notice in the style of the Master of the Fiesole Epiphany an evident similarity with the style of Bigordi, beside whose team he worked on the frescoes of the oratory of San Martino dei Buonomini, painting *The Dream of Saint Martin* (Fig. 3). The list of works by the anonymous painter includes frescoes, domestic panels, but also numerous altarpieces of illustrious provenance,[13] such as the *Volto Santo* of Lucca, formerly in the church of San Marco and today at the Los Angeles County Museum in Los Angeles (Fig. 4), to which Fahy has recently linked five predella compartments (Vienna, Kunsthistorisches Museum),[14] thus providing the painter with a professional profile in line with that which the known documents refer to Filippo di Giuliano.

1. Master of the Fiesole Epiphany
Adoration of the Magi
Fiesole (Florence), San Francesco

2. Master of the Fiesole Epiphany
Coronation of the Virgin
Florence, Galleria dell'Accademia

The polychrome sculpture of the Virgin and Child, contained in the painted tabernacle, has been attributed to Pietro and Giovanni Alemanno, active in Campania in the second half of the 15th century (written communication by Francesco Ortenzi), and was evidently included in the Florentine tabernacle at a time subsequent to its execution, in the place, we believe, of an analogous sculpture that was either lost or had deteriorated: it might also have been a crucifix, however, as in the case of the tabernacle by Bartolomeo di Giovanni in Arezzo (Museo Statale d'Arte Medievale e Moderna), where a 17th-century cross was inserted to replace an older one.[15]

Nicoletta Pons

1) On this argument cf. N. Pons, *Domestic Art in Renaissance Florence*, in *Botticelli to Titian*, exh. cat. (Budapest, 28.10.2009-14.2.2010), eds. D. Sallay, V. Tatrai, A. Vécsey, Budapest 2009, pp. 99-111.

2) G. Dominici, *Regola del governo di cura familiare compilata da Beato Giovanni* Dominici, 1410, ed. Florence 1860, p. 131.

3) For the various types of domestic devotional paintings that were made in Renaissance workshops, cf. Neri di Bicci, *Le ricordanze (1453-1475)*, ed. B. Santi, Pisa 1976.

4) J. K. Lydecker, *The Domestic Setting of the Arts in Renaissance Florence*, Baltimore (Md.), John Hopkins University, PhD. Diss., 1987, pp. 178-179; J. M. Musacchio, *The Madonna and Child, a Host of Saints and Domestic Devotion in Renaissance*

Florence, in *Revaluing Renaissance Art*, eds. G. Heher, R. Shepherd, Cambridge 2000, p. 150; *eadem, Art, Marriage and Family in the Florentine Renaissance Palace*, New Haven 2008, chapter 4.

5) D. Cooper, *Devotion*, in *At Home in Renaissance Italy*, exh. cat. (London, 5.10.2006-7.1.2007), eds. M. Ajmar-Wollheim, F. Dennis, London 2006, p. 194.

6) E. Fahy, *Some Followers of Domenico Ghirlandaio*, London & New York 1976, p. 170; *idem, The Este Predella Panels and Other Works by the Master of the Fiesole Epiphany*, 'Nuovi Studi', 6/7, 2003, 9, p. 24; in both texts he mentions the work in New York, at Piero Tozzi, ca. 1970.

7) The conventional name of the anonymous master was

3. Master of the Fiesole Epiphany
The Dream of Saint Martin
Florence, San Martino dei Buonomini

4. Master of the Fiesole Epiphany
Volto Santo
Los Angeles, Los Angeles County Museum of Art

coined by E. Fahy, *Some Early Italian Pictures in the Gambier-Parry Collection*, 'The Burlington Magazine', CIX, 1967, pp. 133-134.

8) *Ibidem*.

9) N. Pons, *Zanobi di Giovanni e le compagnie di pittori*, 'Rivista d'arte', XLIII, 1991, VII, p. 222.

10) A. Padoa Rizzo, *L'altare della Compagnia dei Tessitori in San Marco a Firenze: dalla cerchia di Cosimo Rosselli al Cigoli*, 'Antichità Viva', XXVIII, 1989, 4, pp. 17-24.

11) N. Pons, *Ricerche documentarie su Jacopo del Sellaio*, in

Invisibile agli occhi, Atti della Giornata di Studio in ricordo di Lisa Venturini (15 December 2005), Pisa 2007, p. 33.

12) G. Gaye, *Carteggio inedito d'artisti dei secoli XIV, XV, XVI*, Florence, I, 1839, p. 580.

13) E. Fahy, *The Este Predella Panels* cit., pp. 22-25, appendix 1.

14) *Ibidem*, pp. 17-22.

15) N. Pons, in *Maestri e botteghe. Pittura a Firenze alla fine del Quattrocento*, exh. cat. (Florence, 16.10.1992-10.1.1993), eds. M. Gregori, A. Paolucci, C. Acidini Luchinat, Milan 1992, pp. 243-244.

Bibliography:

E. Fahy, *Some Followers of Domenico Ghirlandaio*, London & New York 1976, p. 170

Idem, *The Este Predella Panels and Other Works by the Master of the Fiesole Epiphany*, 'Nuovi Studi', 6/7, 2003, 9, p. 24.

Master of the Demidoff Triptych
Emilia?, active in the first half of the 15th century

19a. Saint Michael the Archangel Weighing the Souls and the Devil

Tempera on panel, 41.2 x 22.4 cm (16 $^{1}/_{4}$ x 8 $^{4}/_{5}$ in.)

19b. Saint Raphael the Archangel and Tobias

Tempera on panel, 38.9 x 22.6 cm (15 $^{1}/_{3}$ x 8 $^{7}/_{8}$ in.)

Provenance:
Florence, Carlo De Carlo collection
Florence, Lisa De Carlo collection

Saint Michael is represented with a pair of scales in his left hand with which he weighs the souls of the dead. Psychostasy, or the weighing of souls, was very common in the religion of the ancients, especially that of the Egyptians[1] and also has echoes in the Holy Scriptures. Passages in the books of the prophet Job (31:6) and the prophet Daniel (5:27) refer to the weighing of good and evil actions on the scales of justice, while in the epistle of Jude (1:9) a dispute is mentioned between Michael the Archangel and Satan over possession of the body of Moses, which presents the Archangel as the defender of the souls of the dead. In one pan of the scales there is usually a grindstone, symbolizing the weight of evil, and in the other the soul itself, or, as in this case, two small naked figures representing the good and evil actions of man; depending on how the scales hang the soul is either saved or condemned. This is why the devil is shown trying to manipulate the result, grasping a pan of the scales to make it hang in his favour, but the Archangel defeats him, crushing him with his foot and piercing his jaws with a long lance. The iconography of Satan in the painting is truly unique: usually represented as a semi-human being with monstruous animal-like features (bat's wings, horns, forked tail),[2] a serpent in the book of Genesis (Gen 3:1) or a dragon in Saint John's Apocalypse (cf. Apoc 12:7-9), here instead he appears in the guise of a dog, and I know of no other painting where a similar representation appears.

In the other panel Saint Raphael takes Tobias by the hand and shows him the path they have to take: the Archangel, in fact, has been sent by God to accompany the young man on an adventurous journey to the city of Rages, in the Media, where he must collect the ten talents his father had lent to a relative twenty years earlier (cf. Tb 4:20-21 and 5:1-18). In his right hand Tobias holds the fish, his traditional iconographical attribute,[3] which he has caught in the river Tigris; the gall of the fish would be used to anoint the eyes of his old father, who is blind, and restore his sight (cf. Tob 6:2-4 and 11:7-8).

The faces of the archangels, with their soft features, thin arched eyebrows, small mouths and rounded chins have a feminine aspect; this iconography of the angelic figure, which developed from the middle of the 14th century, was probably influenced by the idea of the angelic woman, but also by the rediscovery of the philosophical doctrine of Pseudo-Dionysius, based on the perfect analogy between the harmony of the universe and female beauty (cf. *De Divinis nominibus*, IV, 7).

The paintings are surrounded by a frame with red, white and green bands. On the back of the *Saint Raphael and Tobias* (Fig. 1) a frame, painted along the left and upper side and today almost completely lost, encloses the fragment of a coat-of-arms and an old label is stuck to it. On the back of the *Saint Michael* (Fig. 2), inside a frame identical to that of the front

depicted along the right and upper edge, is the fragment of a very damaged grey coat-of-arms on a blue field, and written by hand is an old attribution to Pollaiolo. The wooden support, made from a single piece of wood, is in reasonable condition and the state of preservation of the pictorial surface is good.

The two works, together with another panel with Saint Nicholas (Fig. 5) put on auction at Christie's on 31 May 1991 in New York (lot no. 22; 41.5 x 22.3 cm), belonged to a single complex which, as a card fixed to the back of the *Saint Michael* reads, was a big triptych that was in the Demidoff collection: "Saint Georges (École Florentine du 13° Siècle) Gaddi Taddeo. Anciennement partie de un grand triptyque ex. coll. Demidoff 100". The Demidoffs were a noble family from Saint Petersburg. The most important member of the family was Nikolay (Chrirkovitsy, Saint Petersburg, 20 November 1773-Florence, 4 May 1828), entrepreneur, ambassador of the Tsar Alexander I, philanthropist and passionate collector of works of art that he gathered together from 1824 onwards in Palazzo Serristori in Florence and, subsequently, they were moved by his son Anatole I in his new residence, the sumptuous villa at San Donato in Polverosa, at the time just outside the city and built between 1827 and 1831.[4] Following his death between November and December 1828, the heirs asked the Grand Duke of Tuscany permission to export part of the collection to Saint Petersburg; however, in the list of works[5] for which the transfer to Russia was requested and granted the triptych does not appear. From an auction of the collection of Nikolay Demidoff in Paris between 8 and 13 April 1839 (cf. Lugt 15370) it seems that his son Anatole (Saint Petersburg, 5 April 1813-Paris, 29 April 1870) sold some of the works inherited from his father possibly because of their scarce artistic interest, though it has not been possible for me to consult this catalogue. Tullio Dandolo[6] records that in the Catholic chapel of Villa San Donato there was a "panel by Giottino, divided [...] into three compartments, with frames, representing with sublime mastery Angels and Saints surrounding the Madonna and Christ Child", though the rather too general description would suggest leaving for a moment the identification of the triptych with this work. Cesare da Prato,[7] for his part, mentions only three triptychs in this chapel. From the 1860s, as recorded in the list compiled by Lugt (1938-1987) the Demidoff family began progressively to sell off the collections of their Paris residence and the Florentine villas of Quarto and San Donato, though in the catalogues I have consulted there is no trace of the painting: auction in Paris, 13-16 January 1863 (no. 27065), Paul Demidoff; Paris 18 April 1868, Anatole Demidoff (no. 30437); Paris from 21 February to 10 March 1870, Anatole Demidoff (no. 31764). While it has not been possible to see the following auction catalogues: Paris, 3 February 1868, Paul Demidoff (no. 30192); Paris, 1-3 April 1869, Paul Demidoff (no. 31127); Paris, 6 May 1873 (no. 33990). On Anatole's death the entire patrimony was inherited by his nephew Paul (Frankfurt, 9 October 1839-Pratolino, Florence, 26 January 1885), the brother's son, he too named Paul, who between 15 March and 10 April 1880 put on auction the entire collection of works of art and the furnishings of Villa San Donato; but even in the catalogues of this sale the triptych is not mentioned. Part of the collection was moved into his new residence at Pratolino, but not even in the auction catalogue of the villa's furnishing,[8] later inherited by the princes of Yugoslavia, is the work mentioned. Furthermore it has not been possible for me to consult the auction catalogues of the collection of the Russian branch of the Demidoff family, cited by Lugt (no. 8140 in Paris, 2 April 1812), and the heirs: Paris, 6 July 1909 (no. 67817), Budapest, 29-30 March 1918, of Cornelia Demidoff (no. 77748), Amsterdam, 13-16 December 1921 (no. 82889), Rome, 11-16 May 1925 (no. 88594).

It is difficult to hypothesize the original appearance of this triptych; it was probably a cusp-shaped painting, with a representation of the Madonna and Child or the Crucifixion in the centre, the most traditional iconographical subjects, and at the sides two panels with images of the saints which, when they were closed, showed the family arms of the patrons. Or it

1., 2. Master of the Demidoff Triptych
Saint Raphael and Tobias (back)
Saint Michael (back)
Cat. 19

could have been a *retablo*, divided into three compartments, with the saints at the sides. For the time being, since the decorations on the back of the *Saint Michael* and *Saint Raphael* panels do not coincide, one can only conjecture that the two panels were not contiguous. An analysis of the *Saint Nicholas*, presently of unknown location, may provide further clarification. In 1993 the *Saint Michael* was on the English antique market (cf. handwritten annotation on the back of the photograph of the painting PI 0013/5/2 no. 29189 in the Fototeca Zeri), whereas, together with the *Saint Raphael and Tobias*, the following year it was in the Gallery of Giovanni Sarti in Paris (oral communication, Miklós Boskovits); these are therefore two of the last works bought by Carlo De Carlo. Attributed to an anonymous Emilian artist by Federico Zeri (cf. handwritten annotation on the back of the photographs of the paintings in the Fototeca Zeri in the box of Piacenza, Reggio Emilia, Modena; PI 00113/5/3 no. 29190 for the other painting) the two panels were attributed to the circle of Giovanni da Modena in the auction catalogues of the inheritance of Carlo De Carlo (Florence, 11 June 2003, cat. no. 9, and Venice, 17 April 2005, cat. no. 31, pp. 78-79) in which it is hypothesized that they originally formed part of the predella of a polyptych that was later dismembered. Angelo Tartuferi[9] notes in these paintings the influence of Barnaba da Modena and a noticeable neo-Trecento tendency, while Daniele Benati (oral communication) attributes them to a Bolognese painter and identifies echoes of Orazio di Jacopo and the early production of Michele di Matteo. The *Saint Nicholas*, on the other hand, in the catalogue of the 1991 Christie's auction, was generically attributed to the Bolognese School with a dating around 1430.

The style of the paintings is typically Emilian in the expressiveness of the figures, which at times borders on caricature, and the vivid naturalistic interest with which the devil or the fish in the other panel is depicted; these elements, together with the rich colours, like the winey red of Saint Michael's robe, and the fullness of the hair, call to mind a painter like Giovanni da Modena, in particular the figures of God the Father of the cymatium and the mourners of the *tabelloni* of the *Crucifix* in the Pinacoteca Nazionale di Bologna (Fig. 6),[10] executed in the second half of the second decade of the 15th century. The humouristic tone of the expressions is also reminiscent of the Bolognese painter Orazio di Jacopo, in particular an unpublished fragmentary panel of his representing Saint Peter, formerly in a private collection and presently with the antiquarian Grassi in New York. The expanded masses and the clothes of Saint Raphael constructed with a sense of their aplomb, on the other hand, recall the diptych divided between the Fondazione Longhi[11] and a private collection (though formerly Lyon, Aynard collection)[12] of Stefano da Ferrara, datable around the middle of the 1420s; on the basis of these stylistic analogies, therefore, we can date the execution of the panels to the third decade of the 15th century. In the works it seems there is also the influence of painting from Piacenza: the layout and the frame with red, white and green bands, in fact, are similar to the wings of a triptych-reliquary from the Musei Civici di Piacenza, executed in the last decade of the Trecento.[13] The soft, pasty pictorial texture and the preference for colour combinations alternating pastel hues with brightly-coloured tints, together with the outline highlighting the sculptural quality of the figures, instead, reveal stylistic affinities with the works of Antonio de Carro; in particular the *Saint Nicholas*, formerly New York, Christie's 1991, shows physiognomic similarities with that of *Saint Augustine Enthroned between two Angels* (Parma, private collection; Fig. 7),[14] datable on the basis of lost documentation to 1397. However, given the present state of our knowledge it is impossible to arrive at a certain name for the author of these two paintings that are intriguing for the refinement and elegance of the execution, carried out with such meticulousness that it is reasonable to imagine that the artist was also an illuminator: note, for example the devil's fur, painted hair by hair with tiny delicate highlights, the lenticular depiction of the gilded bands on Saint Raphael's tunic, the rippling of the stole of Saint Nicholas's cope, the rendering of the shadows with delicate gradations of colour, and above all the splendid swelling masses of the Archangels' hair, embellished with ribbon, extremely becoming, as if they had

3., 4. Master of the Demidoff Triptych
Saint Michael the Archangel Weighing the Souls and the Devil
Saint Raphael the Archangel and Tobias
Cat. 19

5. Master of the Demidoff Triptych
Saint Nicholas
Private collection

6. Giovanni da Modena
Crucifix
Bologna, Pinacoteca Nazionale

just come out of the hairdresser's. Such careful attention to meticulous representation is also noticeable in the depiction of the elegant and, for the time, fashionable clothes: Saint Michael is wearing a short, close-fitting masculine "vestezola", a tunic characteristic of the 15th century,[15] decorated with acanthus motifs and structured in a way that recalls armour, greaves and pointed iron shoes, while in the other panel Tobias has a child's dress and short stockings with carefully rolled-over tops.[16] The technical execution is also highly refined: note the splendid detail of the wings applied directly on the gold with 'sgraffito' and then punched in the upper part to produce the effect of volume. Saint Michael's movements are gentle and yet at the same time vigorous, like the recoiling of the left arm in an attempt to remove the scales from Satan's reach, or the position of the legs, one outstretched to stay the demon and the other bent to counterbalance the weight of the body. We have here, in conclusion, two extremely evocative and refined works, executed by a painter who is as yet unknown, though was endowed with a strong artistic personality, whom, given the provenance of the complex, I have in the past (2007) referred to provisionally as the Master of the Demidoff Triptych.

Alberto Lenza

7. Antonio de Carro
Saint Augustine Enthroned between two Angels
Parma, private collection

1) Cf. L. Link, *The Devil. A Mask without a Face*, London 1995, pp. 115-119.
2) Cf. J. Baschet, *Diavolo*, in *Enciclopedia dell'Arte Medievale*, V, Rome 1994, pp. 644-650, and L. Link, *The Devil* cit.
3) M. G. Mara, *Raffaele, arcangelo, santo*, in *Enciclopedia Cattolica*, X, Rome 1968, pp. 1366-1368.
4) F. Borroni Salvadori, *I Demidoff collezionisti a Firenze*, 'Annali della Scuola Normale Superiore di Pisa', S. III, XI, 1981, pp. 940, 941.
5) R. Argenziano, *Nicola Demidoff e le sue collezioni nei documenti degli Archivi di Firenze e di San Pietroburgo*, in *I Demidoff a Firenze e in Toscana*, ed. L. Tonini, 1996, pp. 103-143.
6) T. Dandolo, *Panorama di Firenze. La esposizione nazionale del 1861 e la villa Demidoff a San Donato*, Milan 1863, p. 325.
7) C. da Prato, *Firenze ai Demidoff: Pratolino e S. Donato, relazione storica e descrittiva preceduta da cenni biografici sui Demidoff che sino dal secolo XVII esisterono*, Florence 1886, p. 425.
8) *Catalogo di quanto è contenuto nella villa Demidoff a Pratolino, presso Firenze, venduto per ordine di S.A.R. il principe Paolo di Jugoslavia*, Florence, Sotheby's, 21.4.1969.
9) In *Le opere del ricordo. Opere d'arte dal XIV al XVI secolo appartenute a Carlo De Carlo, presentate dalla figlia Lisa*, ed. A. Tartuferi, Florence 2007, pp. 32-37.
10) D. Benati, in *Pinacoteca Nazionale di Bologna. Catalogo generale*, I, *Dal Duecento a Francesco Francia*, Venice 2004, p. 174, entry no. 59.
11) *Idem*, in C. Goméz, *Pasión por la pintura. La Colección Longhi*, Madrid 1998, pp. 65 pl. 6, 155 no. 6.
12) *Colléction Edouard Aynard, Tableaux anciens*, Paris 1913, pl. 31.
13) A. De Marchi, in *Il Gotico a Piacenza. Maestri e botteghe tra Emilia e Lombardia*, eds. P. Ceschi Lavagetto, A. Gigli, Milan 1998, pp. 100-101, 175-176 no. 18.
14) L. Gorni, in *Il Gotico a Piacenza* cit., pp. 109, 192-193 no. 26.
15) Cf. R. Levi Pisetzky, *Storia del Costume in Italia*, I, Milano 1964, p. 314 fig. 145.
16) *Ibidem*, pp. 313 fig. 144, 314 fig. 145, 370-371.

Bibliography:

A. Lenza, in *Le opere del ricordo. Opere d'arte dal XIV al XVI secolo appartenute a Carlo De Carlo, presentate dalla figlia Lisa*, ed. A. Tartuferi, Florence 2007, pp. 32-37

A. Tartuferi, in *Le opere del ricordo. Opere d'arte dal XIV al XVI secolo appartenute a Carlo De Carlo, presentate dalla figlia Lisa*, ed. A. Tartuferi, Florence 2007, p. 11.

WORKSHOP OF THE CLEVELAND CASKET OR WORKSHOP OF THE MAIN BERLIN CASKET

Venice or Ferrara, active from the late 15th to the mid-16th century

20a. Triptych with Scenes from the Life of Christ

Painted and gilded *pastiglia* on a gilded wooden support,
closed 56 x 43.5 cm (22 x 17 1/8 in.), open 56 x 89.5 cm (22 x 35 1/4 in.)

WORKSHOP OF ANDREAS RITZOS (Candia, 1422-1492) OR NIKOLAOS RITZOS (Candia, before 1482-1507)

20b. Icon of the Virgin and Child

Tempera on panel, 16 x 12.6 cm (6 1/4 x 5 in.)

Provenance:
Paris, Guy Ladrière
Florence, Carlo De Carlo collection
Florence, Lisa De Carlo collection

This extraordinary object, unique in its genre and virtually unpublished, bears witness to a whole class of items that have vanished due to their extreme fragility. It is a singular example of a devotional triptych decorated with applied white lead *pastiglia* ornament, which furthermore encloses a contemporary Cretan icon of the Virgin and Child, the image for which the ensemble was probably originally created. The interior surfaces of the triptych present the Life and Passion of Christ in fifteen episodes. Each wing displays three large rectangular scenes: the *Nativity and Annunciation to the Shepherds*, the *Adoration of the Magi* and *Pentecost* on the left, and the *Resurrection, Ascension* and *Assumption* on the right. Across the apices of the triptych wings, following a common precedent in early Italian devotional art, the *Annunciation* takes place within a loggia-like setting. The smaller scenes on the main panel present episodes from the Passion: the *Agony in the Garden,* the *Arrest of Christ, Christ before Annas, Christ before Caiaphas, Christ before Pilate,* the *Flagellation,* and the *Carrying of the Cross*. Above, in the largest compartment, is a complex, multi-figure crucifixion that takes place amidst an open landscape dotted with meandering caravans and distant cities. These central scenes are surrounded by jamb figures of saints: Benedict (or Anthony?), James, Peter and Roch on the left; Scholastica (or Clare?), Paul, Sebastian, and a bishop (?) on the right; and Michael and Christopher below. Lateral pilasters containing unidentifiable prophet figures, much smaller in scale, flank the wings. The main scenes are surmounted by florid Gothic canopies and delineated by colonettes, and the whole ensemble is richly gilded and highlighted with red, blue, green and black polychromy. Extensive zones of silver gilding have now tarnished to a shiny brown-black, and a number of elements including the central figure of the crucified Christ have been lost. Nevertheless, the overall effect is one of great sumptuousness and narrative complexity. Technical, iconographic and documentary evidence suggests that the triptych was created by craft workshops active in Venice or Ferrara at the end of the 15th century. And while the combination of medium and format are unique, the triptych is representative of a range of reliquary-like enclosures created for venerated items of Eastern origin – or of more recent Veneto-Cretan production – that arrived in the Italian peninsula following the fall of Constantinople in 1453.

The wooden core of the triptych, a broadly arched cupboard-like box, is decorated with a proliferation of applied paste decoration known by its Italian name of "pastiglia" or "pasta di muschio/moscho". This technique, often mistakenly confused with the sculpted and gilded gesso decoration found on numerous Trecento paintings and secular wooden caskets, is in fact a type of moulded, applied ornament formed by mixing a white-lead carbonate, obtained by exposing ground lead to vinegar vapour (an ancient process described in Pliny, *Natural History*, IX.vi.6), with sulphate and a binder consisting of egg yolk. Having achieved a doughy consistency, the compound is shaped into individual elements with lead moulds and, while still malleable, is applied to the pre-gilded and tooled wooden support with rabbit-skin glue. Components including bodies, heads, animals, shrubs and the like can thus be layered upon each other in varying combinations, producing original compositions that often diverge from established iconographies. Though the resulting decoration was usually left white, it could be profusely gilded and painted, as in the case of the present object. Another peculiarity of the medium is that it could be scented with musk, producing a pleasing aphrodisiacal odour suitable for small domestic objects. It is unclear whether the present object was once infused with a scent more appropriate to its devotional context.

One virtue of *pastiglia* is that the matrices can be re-used to duplicate forms, as has been noted among groups of *cofanetti* – the small, secular-themed caskets that are the usual vehicle for the technique (Fig. 1). Decorative cornices, landscape elements and even entire figures can be re-employed, cleverly inserted into new compositions. Interestingly, the present triptych re-uses some of its forms to varying effect; the thatched roof above the Nativity scene has been replicated directly below in the *Adoration of the Magi*, as have the serpentine colonettes that separate the events from their subsidiary scene to the right. Numerous figures have been re-used in varying configurations: the rearing horse belonging to one of the

1. Workshop of the Amor-Écouen Casket
Pastiglia cofanetto
London, Victoria and Albert Museum

Magi reappears to the left of the *Crucifixion*; the riders and travelling bindlestiffs are repeated throughout the background; the same apostle figures are duplicated at the *Pentecost*, *Assumption*, and *Dormition*, and countless other landscape and architectural motifs proliferate. While a comparison with motifs found on secular *cofanetti* reveals many similarities, no elements appear to be repeated directly on other objects. Since it is unlikely that moulds would have been produced exclusively for use on one object, and since some figures on the triptych appear awkward or inappropriate to their context, it can be assumed that other devotional *pastiglia* objects were created but have since been lost.

Most surviving *cofanetti* are small, simple boxes made of alder, a hardwood common to the Veneto. Only a dozen or so out of the 115 identified by Patrick de Winter and the 289 identified by Johannes Pommeranz are over 20 centimeters in height. The triptych is thus over three times taller than the average *pastiglia* casket. The few large *pastiglia* compositions that do survive are closer in type to the painted *cassoni*, chests that were a staple of the Renaissance interior. The most famous of these is undoubtedly the *cassone* of Paola Gonzaga now at the Landesmuseum Käntern in Klagenfurt, the hybrid painted and moulded design of which has long been linked to Mantegna (Fig. 2).

In addition to its unprecedented size and format, the triptych is distinguished by its Christological imagery, which is virtually unique among the nearly three hundred catalogued *pastiglia* appliqué caskets. The vast majority of such caskets show scenes from antiquity, either Greek myths from Ovid's *Metamorphoses* or episodes from Roman history, most frequently the tales of Marcus Curtius or Mucius Scaevola from Livy; a handful display scenes from the Old Testament, usually Adam and Eve or the story of Noah. The easy replication of the *pastiglia* technique, however, would have lent itself well to the mass-production of smaller devotional objects, perhaps consisting of amulets or souvenirs similar to lead pilgrim badges, and it is likely that many of the moulds used for the triptych would have been re-employed to create such inexpensive, popular items. The figures of saints in the jambs of the middle section, for example, are comparatively large in scale and would have been readily re-usable. Their presence on the triptych, however, may provide clues as to its original con-

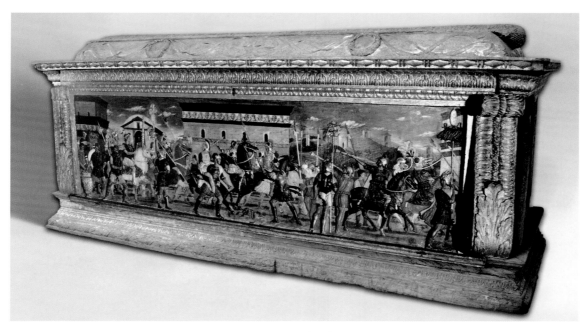

2. *Marriage cassone of Paola Gonzaga*
after designs by Andrea Mantegna
Klagenfurt, Landesmuseum Käntern

3. Workshop of the Cleveland Casket
Pastiglia cofanetto
Cleveland, Cleveland Museum of Art

4. Workshop of the Main Berlin Casket
Pastiglia cofanetto
London, Victoria and Albert Museum

text. Some seem to be placed typologically: Peter is directly next to the *Arrest of Christ*, in which he is present cutting off the ear of Malchus, while Sebastian flanks the scene of the *Flagellation*, an obvious parallel to his own martyrdom. Others must relate to the patrons of the work: the presence of James, Roch and Christopher point towards a pilgrimage context, while a hermit saint resembling Anthony Abbot adjacent to the *Crucifixion* (whose mantle has been left white) may represent Paul of Thebes or, more plausibly, Benedict of Nursia. In the latter case, the female saint opposite could be identified as Saint Scholastica, with whom he is often paired. This might suggest a Benedictine monastery as the original location (see below). The absence of any Franciscan or Dominican saints seems to preclude the triptych's relation to a mendicant order.

The versatility of *pastiglia* elements renders the identification of certain scenes somewhat difficult. The lowest scene on the left-hand wing, for example, had previously been identified as *Christ among the Doctors*, which would fit chronologically into the infancy narrative initiated above. However, the figure in the centre of the composition is undoubtedly Mary surmounted by the Holy Spirit, indicating that the scene in fact represents the *Pentecost*, which jars with an otherwise chronological progression between the three sections of the triptych. The apostle figures, which incongruously include among them a woman and a hooded hermit, are repeated in slightly different positions for the *Ascension* and *Assumption* on the opposite wing. If not the result of an oversight, these idiosyncrasies might indicate that the triptych was intended for viewing at a distance, upon an ecclesiastical altar rather than in a private devotional context.

Comparison with the numerous surviving secular *pastiglia* caskets makes it possible to suggest a locale of production for the object, though the precise circumstances of its creation – probably spurred by the arrival of the Cretan icon – cannot yet be ascertained. From De Winter's seminal identification of seven distinct *pastiglia* workshops responsible for the secular caskets, two were involved in the largest and most complex ensembles.[1] These were the Workshop of the Main Berlin Casket and the Workshop of the Cleveland Casket, each of which produced relatively large caskets with multiple scenes on each face, divided by classicizing pilasters or floral colonettes (Figg. 3-4). An example of such a casket, recently sold at auction (Sotheby's, London, 7 December 2010, lot 31), bears a type of polychromy reminiscent of that found on the triptych. It was undoubtedly a group of artisans related to these two workshops – perhaps their direct forerunners – that produced the virtuoso *pastiglia* decoration of the triptych.

The intriguing stylistic combination of *all'antica* elements, including the armour of the soldiers, the putti on Christ's tomb and the muscular, Donatello-like horses in the *Crucifixion*, with the Northern character of the *Annunciation to the Shepherds* iconography, its gesturing herdsmen and lamb-nursing *bergère* typical of French manuscript illumination, is intriguing. Furthermore, the florid Gothic canopies that surmount each compartment are not found on any of the secular-themed caskets. This is perhaps the result of a Gothic style of decoration being deemed more suitable for a devotional object, though it could equally point to an earlier date, perhaps significantly earlier than the year 1503, which is given as a starting point by De Winter for the production of *cofanetti*. Stylistically, these canopies seem to derive from the intricate wooden frames carved by Cristoforo da Ferrara for altarpieces painted by the Vivarini workshop in Murano (Fig. 5).

It is interesting to note that the earliest mention of "pasta di moscho" in Italy (in French inventories it is documented even earlier in the century) appears in connection with an artisan from the North. A certain Carlo di Monlione of Brittany, active at the Este court in Ferrara in the 1450s, is recorded as having produced numerous "capsetine" (cases) and "cofaniti" (caskets) but also "ancone" (devotional images) and "cornixati" (frames), all in "pasta di moscho" (Pommeranz, docs. 9-13). Perhaps he was responsible for importing a distinctly Northern flavour into the conception of the triptych. The accomplished painter Cosimo Tura and the miniaturist Giorgio d'Alemagna often assisted Monlione in gilding and painting such objects including, in 1452, a panel "con figure del nostro Signore Dio e Nostra Dona e passione e altri lavorieri de moscho," which might very well have resembled the present object, if not for the improbably early date. Later Este inventories of 1493 and 1494 further record a number of intriguing items that confirm the use of the medium for devotional objects and frames (of which our triptych is both), including a "quadreto depincto cornisato intorno cum paste cum un Christo" and "un'altra anchona in uno quadro di legno dorato cum Nostra Donna facta di pasta da odore" (Pommeranz, docs. 26, 28).

If the topmost flanking saints in the triptych can indeed be identified as Benedict and Scholastica, and if the area of production can be narrowed to the Po Valley, it may be possible to suggest a link with the Benedictine abbey of Pomposa, which stands in the marshes of the Po estuary some 30 kilometers east of Ferrara. Pomposa had easy access to the sea, links with the Venetian colonies in the Eastern Mediterranean, and was a centre of humanist learning in the later 15th century. Alternatively, the Benedictine community of Polirone near Mantua, somewhat further inland but similarly undergoing a revival around 1500, may

5. Antonio Vivarini, Giovanni d'Alemagna, Cristoforo da Ferrara
Altarpiece of the Rosary (detail of frame)
Venice, San Zaccaria, chapel of San Tarasio

6. School of Andreas Ritzos
Virgin and Child
Athens, Benaki Museum

have had a connection to the object. Further study, both of the object and its little-known medium, will undoubtedly produce a more definitive localization.

No discussion of the triptych can be complete without a consideration of the Byzantinizing icon that stands at its centre. It is a combination of a generic type in which Christ and his mother tenderly embrace, known as the *Glykophilousa* or Virgin of Tenderness, with the *Amolyntos* or Virgin of the Passion, in which Christ looks over his shoulder at an angel bearing a cross as he clasps his mother's hand and his sandal falls loose. The latter was popularized by the Veneto-Cretan painter Andreas Ritzos, who lived in Candia from 1451 to 1492 and worked predominantly for the Italian export market, as signed examples in Fiesole (Museo Bandini) and Parma (Galleria Nazionale), as well as others in Bari (San Nicola) and Ferrara (Santa Maria in Vado) attest. The merging of these two types, with the additional detail of Christ holding a scroll in his right hand, is an innovation likewise linked to the painter, which also appears in numerous Cretan icons exported to Italy. The greatest of these is undoubtedly that in the church of the Ognissanti at Trani attributed to Andreas himself, though versions also survive in Milan (ex-Mancinelli-Scotti collection) and in Ravenna (Museo Nazionale, inv. 4460). Another version, identical but larger in scale, exists in the Velimezis collection at the Benaki Museum, Athens (Fig. 6). The present icon, simplified through the omission of the falling sandal and other details, appears slightly later in date and may possibly be by Andreas' son, Nikolaos, active around the turn of the 16th century (before 1482-1507). If this is the case, it would favour a slightly later dating of the triptych and a distancing from the workshop of Carlo di Monlione in mid-15th-century Ferrara. Regardless of its precise date, the icon's neat insertion into its frame (its painted surface has not been cut down) and the clear popularity of its type in Renaissance Italy suggest that it is original to the creation of the triptych, and not a later interpolation.

Nicholas Herman

1) P. M. de Winter, *A little-known creation of Renaissance decorative arts: The White Lead Pastiglia Box*, 'Saggi e memorie di storia dell'arte', 12, 1984, pp. 7-42, 133-170; J. Pommeranz, *Pastigliakästchen: Ein Beitrag zur Kunst- und Kulturgeschichte der italienischen Renaissance*, Münster & New York 1995; L. Martini, L. Foi, *Cofanetti in pastiglia del Rinascimento italiano*, exh. cat. (Brescia, Brixiantiquaria, 2005), Brescia 2005; M. D. Mazzoni, *Cofanetti in pastiglia del Rinascimento: Modelli, tecnica artistica, collezionismo e repliche*, 'OPD Restauro', 14, 2002, pp. 89-98; M. Zaccagnini, *Pastiglia Boxes: Hidden Treasures of the Italian Renaissance*, exh. cat. (Miami, Lowe Art Museum, 2002), Miami 2002; M. Cattapan, *I pittori Andrea e Nicola Rizo da Candia*, 'Thesaurismata', 10, 1973, pp. 238-282; M. Chatzidakis, *Les debuts de l'école cretoise et la question de l'école dite italo-grecque*, in *Mnemosynon Sophias Antoniade*, Venice 1974, pp. 169-211; N. Chatzidakis, *Icons: The Velimezis Collection*, Athens 1997, no. 2, pp. 74-77; Idem, *From Candia to Venice: Greek Icons in Italy, 15th-16th Centuries*, Athens 1993, nos. 6, pp. 42-44, 40, 164-165.

Bibliography:
J. Corsi, in *Le opere del ricordo. Opere d'arte dal XIV al XVI secolo appartenute a Carlo De Carlo, presentate dalla figlia Lisa*, ed. A. Tartuferi, Florence 2007, pp. 38-41.

Master of the Dishevelled Crucifixes

Florence, late 15th-early 16th century

21. Crucifix

Carved wood, 49 x 42 cm (19 $1/4$ x 16 $1/2$ in.)

Provenance:
Florence, Carlo De Carlo collection
Florence, Lisa De Carlo collection

The sculpture appears without the polychrome decoration that originally invariably completed this kind of object, and without the loincloth, which should be imagined as a piece of fabric impregnated with a chalk and glue paste. The carved body is essentially intact: with the exception of some of the phalanges of the fingers, even the tiniest and most fragile parts, like the locks of hair or the delicately arranged feet, are well-preserved. In some areas the work has suffered damage caused by wood-boring insects, with tiny holes in the chest and on the flanks of the crucifix, some of which have been eliminated by cleaning and restoration work. The arms – separately carved obviously – were originally articulated, that is, it was possible to drop them along the sides of the body of Christ, making them revolve on linchpins inserted into the shoulders of the figure. This mechanism, very widespread from the Trecento onwards, had the purpose of making possible a sort of small sacred representation in the course of Holy Week liturgies, when the figure could be made to look like a deposed Christ. A particularly celebrated example of a 'crucifix with moving arms' is the one by Donatello in Santa Croce, where the mechanism was put back in working order on the occasion of a restoration. In the crucifix presented here the movement of the arms was also renewed by a restoration.

The small sculpture under examination has distinctive stylistic characteristics that enable us to trace its origin immediately to the time of that intense production of crucifixes in Florence that took place between the last years of the 15th century and the early decades of the following century. One of the main reasons for such a prolific output was the incidence of devotional prayers that developed in the city around the figure and the preaching of Girolamo Savonarola. It has been observed that never before had so many wooden crucifixes been made by Florentine carvers, nor would so many be ever subsequently produced.[1] It was, therefore, a large-scale and articulated production that involved numerous workshops, a phenomenon that has not yet been comprehensively researched. On the occasion of a recent auction,[2] the piece presented here was tentatively linked to the artists Giuliano (ca. 1445-1516) and Antonio (ca. 1455-1534) da Sangallo, an attribution that is unconvincing since the wooden sculptures of the two masters – like Giuliano's magnificent crucifix for the church of the Santissima Annunziata in Florence – exhibit decidedly squarer, powerful, almost muscular forms, where sinewy masses are emphatically thrown into relief. In comparison with the heroic conception of the Sangallo crucifixes, our piece has a more tapered structure, with slender proportions, a less emphatic plasticism that is attentive rather to pictorial effects and the subtle play of chiaroscuro.

1. Master of the Dishevelled Crucifixes
Crucifix (detail)
Prato, oratory of Sant'Antonio Abate

2. Master of the Dishevelled Crucifixes
Crucifix (detail)
Florence, Museo dell'Opera del Duomo

The first to introduce Florentine sculptors to such tendencies – which aimed at a sentimental and sorrowful rendering of the figure of Christ on the Cross – had been Benedetto da Maiano (1442-1497), who in his final years had executed the splendid crucifix for the high altar of the cathedral of Santa Maria del Fiore, with its certainly vigorous yet extremely slender figure, the small head, expressive and melancholy, lying abandoned on the right shoulder. In the wake of this and other crucifixes by Benedetto, variations on the theme multiplied in the best Florentine workshops dedicated to wooden sculpture. The most well-known and easily recognizable case is probably that of Baccio da Montelupo (1469-ca. 1535), the author, among other things, of the grandiose crucifix for San Marco, today hanging in the chapter house, and the small crucifix that belonged to Savonarola himself (today in a cell of the same complex of San Marco), evidence of Baccio's personal involvement in the tumultuous political and religious events associated with the figure of the Dominican friar which subsequently forced him to flee to Bologna. These are works in which the artist chooses to retain the more athletic aspects of the 15th-century tradition, for example the distension of the ribcage, at the same time emphasizing dramatic characteristics like the half-open mouth or the evidently suffering expression. To find subtler effects, a more pronounced softness in the play of light and shadow, a more refined emotional tone, we must turn to the products of other less well-known workshops working in Florence during these years: for example the one responsible for a number of crucifixes of varying size that have been grouped together only recently, characterized by leaner and more youthly builds, which in the moment of abandonment to death hint at an elegant twisting of the figure on the Cross.[3] In the work of this anonymous master we notice perhaps a certain drop in quality among the larger examples, where the carving in certain areas seems to become more laboured and repetitive (for example in the crucifix of the Badia di Passignano, or in that of the church of Santa Maria at Panzano in Chianti), and the smaller ones, some of which are modelled with remarkable skill, to the extent that for the finest of the group – which possibly served as a reference model for all the others – the name of the young Michelangelo has been authoritatively advanced, around the year 1495.[4]

As regards the crucifix that interests us here, finally, it appears to have many similarities with

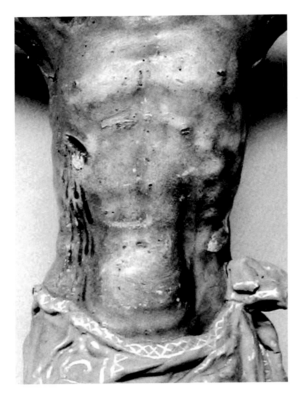

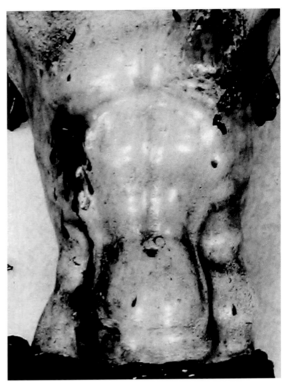

3. Master of the Dishevelled Crucifixes
Crucifix (detail)
Florence, church of San Lorenzo

4. Master of the Dishevelled Crucifixes
Crucifix (detail)
Florence, church of Santa Maria di Peretola

the group just mentioned, in its long-limbed and elastic build, in its lean yet vigorous muscularity, and in the vibrant play of light on the modelled surface. However, it also has characteristics that set it apart from that series, in particular the harsh expressiveness that is transmitted to the entire figure and pervades it from the tensed delicate feet up to the dense undulating locks of hair, rendered with an impressionistic style that confers to them an almost electric quality.

In the search for other sculptures that have analogous stylistic traits it is worthwhile consulting that fundamental compendium of Tuscan crucifixes put together forty years ago by Margrit Lisner, where the works produced in the decades straddling the late 15th and early 16th century alone make up more than a third of the illustrations, evidence of how widespread the Florentine production was in that period, both in the monumental format and in smaller sizes for private use. And precisely within these pages, at figure 239, we come across a work with characteristics that perfectly coincide with our own, to the point that we can confidently assert that these sculptures came from the same workshop. This is the crucifix housed in the oratory of Sant'Antonio Abate at Prato, identical in the thin pointed face (Fig. 1), the unkempt hair, the stubbly beard, and the tensed muscles of the slender body of Christ. Lisner gathered around this sculpture a substantial group of crucifixes that she considered came from the same workshop, but perhaps because she had insufficient space to reproduce them all and because many of the pieces were weighed down by modern repaintings, her proposal seems to have gone unnoticed in more recent studies.[5] In point of fact, after careful re-examination, the catalogue put together by the German scholar appears to be entirely convincing and stylistically compact, presenting us with a sculptor specialized in the carving of crucifixes who must have been highly esteemed at the beginning of the 16th century both in Florence (where he worked for some of the most important churches in the city) and its outlying area. Belonging to our master, therefore, is a crucifix from the Opera del Duomo formerly exhibited in the Sagrestia delle Messe in Santa Maria del Fiore and then in the Baptistery (Fig. 2, presently under restoration), another in the Cappella delle Stimmate in San Lorenzo (Fig. 3), a third in San Giuseppe, then, going beyond the city walls, that of the high altar of Santa Maria di Peretola (Fig. 4), the one previously mentioned from the oratory of Sant'Antonio Abate in Prato and the one in the sacristy of the monastery of San Vincenzo Ferrer in the same city, and lastly one in Santa Maria a Cortenuova, near Empoli.[6] The same ideas appear in all of the works mentioned: the highly pronounced emphasis of the abdominal muscles, and the distinctively shaggy and splintery rendering of the hair and beard, to the point that if one wished to coin an appropriate name for the anonymous carver one might call him the "Master of the Dishevelled Crucifixes"; it may be noted, lastly, that many of these pieces have movable arms. It could also be mentioned that, as in the case mentioned above, here too we notice at times a certain harshness in the larger specimens (those of Peretola and Cortenuova), a quality that is absent in the more elegant and composed crucifixes destined for private devotion (such as in the cell of a friar or the bedchamber of a layman): among these it is certainly the piece under examination, which combines extreme elegance with an intense expressiveness, that reaches the highest quality.

Aldo Galli

1) M. Lisner, *Holzkruzifixe in Florenz und in der Toskana von der Zeit um 1300 bis zum frühen Cinquecento*, Munich 1970, pp. 96-97.

2) Semenzato, Firenze, *Eredi Carlo De Carlo*, 15 December 2001, no. 8, 11 June 2003, no. 95 (in both cases as "Scultore fiorentino nell'ambito dei Sangallo").

3) *Proposta per Michelangelo giovane: un crocifisso in legno di tiglio*, catalogue, ed. G. Gentilini, Turin 2004, pp. 77-87; E. Fadda, in *Il crocifisso di Badia a Passignano: tecnica, conservazione e considerazioni critiche*, Florence 2004, pp. 21-31, who orients them in the follow-up to the late Maianesque production, referring to the Del Tasso family and in particular to the figure of Leonardo, who was heir to Benedetto's workshop in 1497.

4) *Proposta per Michelangelo* cit. For an attribution to Andrea Sansovino see the opinion of Margrit Lisner, *Osservazioni sulla mostra "Proposta per Michelangelo giovane" al Museo Horne di Firenze: opera di Michelangelo o di Andrea Sansovino?*, 'Arte Cristiana', XCII, 2004, pp. 421-426.

5) M. Lisner, *Holzkruzifixe* cit., pp. 96-97 and 109, note 190 and 191.

6) I have not yet had the opportunity to verify a figure of Christ Deposed under an altar of the church of San Paolo at Pistoia, this too mentioned by Lisner.

Bibliography:
A. Galli, in *Le opere del ricordo. Opere d'arte dal XIV al XVI secolo appartenute a Carlo De Carlo, presentate dalla figlia Lisa*, ed. A. Tartuferi, Florence 2007, pp. 42-45, cat. 7 (from which this entry is taken).